A very personalized approach

Stacy really works to enable you with the tools you need to improve your health and wellbeing. After working with her for a few months I feel incredibly empowered and equipped to not only deal with but live with my anxiety.

Great Insights

I have felt through my interactions with Stacy that not only can she offer great insights, I have felt that she has genuinely cared about my situations and practicing the methods she has offered even in the short amount of time that they have been utilized, I noticed an improvement. If you are dealing with a lot of internal anxiety and are willing to put in the effort, Stacy is a great individual to work with.

Wonderful Therapist

Stacy is a wonderful therapist. She listens to everything you say, and I really like her new age approach to therapy.

Supportive and compassionate!

Stacy has been a wonderful asset in my healing process, allowing me space to talk as needed and giving advice and some really wonderful techniques to use along the way. She seems to always have the right tool at hand whenever I need it. I also really appreciate her mindfulness techniques that she shares with me.

Top Notch!

Stacy is attentive and gave me a lot of tools that made this method of therapy seem a lot more effective than I thought it would be. She is knowledgeable & asks the right kind of questions to steer you in the right direction & help you look inward at what needs to be looked at. She has been a great help!

Perspective

Stacy always has another way of looking at things that allows me to rethink and process the situation. Giving me tools to help me be successful in all areas of my life.

Great to talk to

Stacy was really helpful with listening and addressing all points. She would give me exercises to reinforce my self-compassion and they were helpful.

Elegant Way of Distilling Emotions

Stacy has a wonderful way of distilling what feels overwhelming and complicated into a manageable way of thinking. She's helped me begin to organize my thoughts and asks questions that I've not thought about before - ones that I think will bring a lot of clarity. I feel supported and cared about.

Due to the nature of my work, client's wish to remain anonymous and their identities will be protected

Your
Empowered Soul

A Natural
Pathway to Healing
Anxiety and Depression

Stacy K. Musial, LCSW
Fort Collins, Colorado

Disclaimer

The content of this book is for general informational purposes only. It is not meant to be used, nor should it be used, to diagnose or treat any medical condition or to replace the services of your physician or other healthcare provider. The advice and strategies contained in the book may not be suitable for all readers. Please consult your healthcare provider for any questions that you may have about your own medical situation. Neither the author, publisher, IIN nor any of their employees or representatives guarantees the accuracy of information in this book or its usefulness to a particular reader, nor are they responsible for any damage or negative consequence that may result from any treatment, action taken, or inaction by any person reading or following the information in this book.

Printed in the United States of America

Editorial supervision: Sheryl Harrell
Book cover Co-Creative Mandalas image, "Empowered", credit:
www.cocreativementoring.com
Professional photo credit on back cover: Robyn Ivy Photography

ISBN Number 978-0-578-40185-0
Library of Congress Cataloguing-in-Publication Data
2018912219
Your empowered soul: a natural pathway to healing anxiety and depression

Acknowledgements

It is my hope and desire that this book reach and help many people across the world.

I am grateful to my dear friend, mentor, coach and editor, Sheryl Harrell. I have personally worked with Sheryl for over 16 years in many capacities. She has played an integral role in my life, being a conduit to healing many layers of pain in my life. She has encouraged me to keep moving forward and supported me in my quest to create the life I desire. She reminded me to trust myself and to speak my truth. She encouraged me to write this book and continues to support me in immeasurable ways.

I am so appreciative of my IIN accountability partner, Lauren Bahr. Her passion was contagious. She continued to support me and my vision, encouraged me to get my message out there and cheered me on every step of the way.

I'd like to thank my dad, Steve and stepmother Laurie Musial, for always supporting me and teaching me to never give up on my dreams and for my dad encouraging me to maintain my unrelenting optimism. I am grateful to my son Andre Musial. Without him, my path may have looked different. He has inspired me to be the best person I can be and to create an example he can be proud of.

I would like to acknowledge my soul dog, Sprout, who sat by my feet and loved me every step of the way during this book writing process.

I would like to recognize my mom, Sheila Underwood, for always believing that I would follow my childhood dream and write a book. I am so grateful for all of my clients for teaching me more about myself and helping me grow and expand my own awareness. The commitment toward your own growth has been a true inspiration to me.

I would like to give a huge shout-out to my family for creating safe space to enjoy a whole-food, plant-based lifestyle.

CONTENTS

INTRODUCTION

Finding Your Path to Health

"Love is at the heart of the world, just as it is at the heart of your life. Your relationships with your lover, your family, your friends, and the world around you define the quality of your emotional wholeness and reflect your relationship with yourself." ~Sebastian Pole

Sally came into my office one day for a scheduled appointment. She sat down, her face looked sunken and sullen, she was emotionally numb. Sally was obese and despite her best efforts, very disconnected from her body. She revealed that she had been depressed for many years and her anxiety was through the roof. She cried at the drop of a hat and couldn't understand why. During the initial assessment, I asked a lot of questions about her lifestyle, including her diet, exercise, relationships, including the one she had with herself, spirituality, and creative outlets. I asked her about how she loved herself and took care of her. She was not sure what this meant. She came to me because she knew I was going to look at the big picture. I will take you through her story, as you navigate your way through this book.

Many people come to me thinking they are broken and need to be fixed. This is just not true. We are whole already, needing a little love and nurturing to empower and heal for the sake of our soul's path. Once we learn the tools we need, we are set for great soul development. Sometimes, it's just a matter of not knowing what we don't know in the scheme of things. We are taught many things on the path and it is up to us to decipher the messages received by societal standards or placed there by corporations that lead us to believe that we are lacking something if we don't do it "that way." I am here to help you learn to honor your body, listen to your soul and create the life you are really meant to live.

In today's medical model, we are only focused on the symptoms associated with physical and emotional illnesses. The symptoms are treated primarily with pills. The problem with this approach is that it is not getting to the root of the bigger problem. Mental health issues are rising dramatically. In fact, the Diagnostic and Statistical Manual (DSM, aka, the book that clinicians use to diagnose mental health disorders) has grown exponentially since its first printing in 1952. At the time of the first printing it contained 132 pages and 128 diagnoses. The current edition, the DSM-5, has grown to 947 pages and a total of 541 diagnostic categories, an increase of nearly 160 categories compared to the DSM-4 published in 2000. At the time of this writing, according to the Centers for Disease Control and Prevention, suicide rates have increased by 30% since 1999! In 2016, there were 45,000 deaths by suicide making suicide the top 10 cause of death in the U.S.

According to the National Institute of Mental Health, anxiety disorders are the most common mental illness in the U.S., affecting 40 million adults ages 18 and older or 18% of the population. In any given year, major depression is the leading cause of disability in the U.S. for ages 15 to 44.3 and affects more than 15 million American adults, or about 6.7 percent of the U.S. population ages 18 and older. Why are these numbers so staggering? This is a growing concern in the U.S. and around the world.

What is going on? Why are people choosing to take their own life at such an alarming rate? Why are so many people so sick, depressed and anxious? How can there be such a long list of mental health diagnoses that we have never seen before? Are we destined to be pathologically sick? There has to be a root cause to all of this! I truly believe in my heart and my soul that we are not meant to live this life in pain and suffering. We are meant to love and serve our soul's purpose. We are meant to create the life we want (whether you can see that yet or believe it).

Over the past few decades more and more people are prescribed antidepressants such as Prozac, Zoloft, Xanax, and Ativan. These hard drugs have long term implications for people. They not only suppress the will to live fully, they numb you out to the point where your emotions are not accessible. In turn, when someone is coming off of these medications, withdrawal causes emotions that have been suppressed for so long to erupt uncontrollably. In fact, the Citizen Commission on Human Rights and Harvard University's Dr. Joseph Glenmullen warn that antidepressants might explain the rash of school shootings and mass suicides over the last decade. People taking them "feel like jumping out of their skin. The irritability and impulsivity can make people suicidal or homicidal." A study of 950 acts of violence committed by people taking antidepressants found 362 murders, 13 school shootings, 5 bomb threats or bombings, 24 acts of arson, 21 robberies, 3 pilots who crashed their planes and more than 350 suicides and suicide attempts.

It is easy to believe that psychotropic medications are the way to go because that is what the pharmaceutical industry would like you to believe. But the data and evidence clearly show that there is a direct correlation between antidepressants, violent behavior, and other mental health issues. Taking these drugs may provide temporary relief but they are not a pathway to lasting happiness. Our human forms are perfectly built to heal themselves and work toward realizing our life purpose. It is up to each of us to fully understand that. But it requires a lifetime of discovery.

Maybe you were prescribed antidepressants because you were in a bad relationship. Trust that there is a better way to find happiness and peace of mind. Perhaps, it's about looking within and discovering

3

yourself, finally finding your voice, healing your past, or learning to listen to your partner. Perhaps, you are struggling with anxiety and need to discover your strengths. Whatever the reason, it's not going to be found with medication. We are being subjected to the medical model, that prescribes medications that disempower us and tells us there's something "wrong" with us. There's nothing wrong with us. We are not deficient of Prozac or other medications.

Instead, perhaps, you just need the strength to make changes in your life and to honor the life that you have. Being soul empowered and being in touch with emotions is part of the human experience. Emotions are meant to be embraced and honored. Learning to get to the root cause of suffering is within your control. Finding what's underneath the pain, learning to validate yourself, releasing blocks, physically healing, and living a life of joy, peace and passion is what you truly deserve. I will help you with your journey. I will hold your hand as you read this book and do the exercises. I will support you and your soul will thank you. I know, because I have been there.

My journey to discover my own soul's purpose hasn't been an easy one, but I wouldn't change a thing. It has made me who I am and has lead me to write this book. At age 28, I was in school for my bachelor's and then my master's degree, a single mom with very poor eating habits, overweight, didn't exercise, smoked regularly and probably drank way too much. I had anxiety, depression and a lot of trauma that I had never faced in my life, not to mention Hashimoto's, an autoimmune thyroid disease. I found myself alone. Even though I had friends I didn't feel connected to anyone. I found myself crying and feeling insecure. The truth was, I didn't know who I was or what I wanted from life. I thought life happened to me, and I didn't have any control or say in the outcome. I was lost. I decided to seek help. I found a doctor and told him how I was feeling. He prescribed Prozac. I took the prescription, but something felt off and wrong. Something told me not to fill the prescription.

I have always had a holistic point of view, so I knew there was more to life than taking Prozac. I felt that there was more to healing. I found myself wondering if there was more to life and wanted to know

4

how to get there. I wasn't sure how to get from where I was to where I wanted to be. I didn't know where that was or even what that looked like. And so, my journey began. I started searching for information and reading everything I could get my hands on about meditation, nutrition, natural healing, energy work, exercise and finding meaning and purpose in life. I couldn't get enough! Once I started to apply what I was learning, magical shifts started occurring in my life. I started to feel good! I started with my physical body and cleansed all of the toxins I had been putting in my body over the years. I quit smoking and drinking excessively. I learned about nutrition and discovered that what I put in my body was more crucial than I could've ever imagined. I started setting goals for myself. I began exercising. I started meditating and looking within and healing blocks that I hadn't looked at because I was afraid to look within. Looking within? What is that? When I learned not to fear the emotions, everything changed! I learned to love myself. I discovered what I wanted in life. I learned to stand in my truth.

As I was going through this process, I was also on the path to get my social work degree and I discovered I really wanted to practice psychotherapy. I wanted to help people discover more about themselves and discover the gem that they hold for themselves. I wanted to help people love themselves and their life! Once we start peeling the onion and the layers of hurt, resentments and pain, we discover authentically who we are, and learn to embrace that.

And guess what? Life hands you more peace and love than you ever imagined, because now you're open to it. The truth is we are all love. When we start showing up for ourselves and embracing the love that is our SOUL truth we start experiencing and seeing the world from a different perspective.

It is my mission and intention to show you all the tools that have worked for my clients and me. I want you to truly love yourself and live the soul empowered life that you are meant to live. It is my belief that in order to teach, I must use the tools. There's nothing in this book that I have not applied in my own life. You'll see, as you read through the book, how Sally's life has changed and how yours can too!

We are at an exciting time on this planet. Many of us are waking up to a new understanding about our true purpose. Let me help you discover your soul empowered life. I will hold your hand as you clear what has been holding you back so that you can live a life of love, peace, truth and aliveness!

How to Use This Book

This book identifies the main components in helping to heal depression and anxiety from my perspective. Each chapter builds on the next one and depending on where you are starting from in your health journey, you may want to skip to what applies to you. For instance, if you've been eating clean already, you may want to learn how to support your gut or about detoxing with an elimination diet.

In Chapter 1 you will begin to open up to your soul's desires for creating the life you want to live, what you want to attain from reading this book, and an exercise to expand your aspirations for healing and for your life.

In Chapter 2 you will learn all about thoughts and how to manage them through awareness. You will learn many tools and techniques to build your relationship with your thoughts.

In Chapter 3 you will learn about your emotional self. You will learn new strategies to build a stronger connection with your emotions and heal unprocessed feelings.

In Chapter 4 you will learn about clean eating and its implications for healing depression and anxiety. It contains many ideas and suggestions for making changes in your overall lifestyle.

In Chapter 5 you will learn about gut health. You'll dive deeper into how gut health affects your brain and what you can do about it.

In Chapter 6 you will learn how detoxification strategies help release toxic buildup that contributes to anxiety and depression.

In Chapter 7 you will learn about more approaches for balancing your system and naturally overcoming anxiety and depression.

In Chapter 8, you will learn powerful processes to empower your soul, manifest your desires, and open your heart to the love that you are.

Disclaimer: This book includes some out-of-box tools and practices. Please use your discretion and listen to your body. Use the tools that feel right for you and honor your body and your process.

Are you ready? Let's go!

CHAPTER ONE

Your Soul's Desires

"You have the power within your reach to create what you desire."
— Lailah Gifty Akita, Think Great: Be Great!

If you're going on a cross country round trip, most likely you'll need a map or some sort of GPS device to get there. Even if you're okay with scenic routes and detours, it's important to have a sense of where you're headed so you'll know when you've arrived. It also matters to know why you want to go there. The same holds true for reaching your goals in life. Think about what you want in life and why you want it. It is important because if you don't have your *why* in mind, it's easy to forget what you're going toward. So, why do you want to feel good and get healthy? How has anxiety or depression been holding you back? Knowing your why will help you reach your goal and know when you arrive at your destination. Knowing your why is your motivator and helps keep you going toward creating the life that you envision and deserve.

When you know your why you are taking a proactive approach to your life.

As I began my work with Sally, we explored her why. At first, she was unsure, as she had never been asked this question. She never gave it much thought. In fact, she believed society knew the rules and she had to follow them. She had no idea what she really wanted or why she wanted it. Many people think what they are looking for is 'out there' and expect life to just happen to them. They are living on autopilot and are unconscious. When you take the proactive approach and live on purpose, you'll reach your destination because you've created it from your intentions and your actions. Knowing your why will help you gain clarity about what you want. When you make decisions and choices in your life, it brings a new sense of confidence and relief because you know which direction you really want to go. Your why is your emotional driving force. What emotion is underneath your why? How will taking the steps toward achieving health and living a life free of depression and anxiety make you feel? Do you want a life of freedom from the chains of your negative emotions? Do you want to live your soul's purpose and achieve your goals? Are you ready to finally let go of what keeps you stuck? Do you want to feel empowered? How will these changes make you feel? Is it the feeling that you're after, a sense of wellbeing? Deep down your soul knows that you are here for something more. You picked up this book for a reason. What is your reason?

Through some deep questioning, Sally was able to dig deep into her soul and discover her why and what was important to her. Your why is your soul telling you what is important for you. It is your truth and it's only for you. Everyone's why is different. Dig deep to find your why. Here are some questions to get you started:

1. What is truly important to me?
2. What will I gain from taking these steps?
3. What energizes me to feel good?
4. How does feeling good FEEL in my body?

Now, why do you want to overcome depression and anxiety? Are you ready to live the life your soul intends you to live? Setting intentions will help you gain clarity. The why is your overarching theme for what you want, and the intentions allow you to set your sights on the specifics. There's a lot of power in setting intentions, because once you set an intention it starts to move your energy in the direction that you want it to go. This is your road map. The universe hears you and starts bringing in the pieces to help you manifest your intentions. What is deep within your heart? What do you whole-heartedly want to create?

Sally came into my office feeling timid and doubtful that this could work for her. She thought that she wasn't going to get better because she had always felt anxious and depressed and didn't know any other way to feel. She had no idea what was possible for her. We discussed how her doubts and fears were getting in the way of her goals and we began to shift her focus. Do you notice any doubts or limiting beliefs that question your ability to get well and live the soul empowered, vibrant life that you deserve? Let's shift your attention from doubts and fears. I invite you to imagine a box or container, of any shape or size, and imagine putting that doubt, fear and uncertainty and anything else that does not serve you right now into the container. Put a lid on it and even lock it or put chains around it. Now, put it away, on a shelf, in the closet or toss it in to the ocean. Remember that your container is always there. Your doubts and your fears are always available to you if you need them. So are the hope, faith and love that you can choose to have for yourself. Your life is so much more than your negative emotions and the limiting beliefs and fears that drive those emotions. You deserve to know this.

How do you want to live in alignment with your soul's purpose? Whether or not you have figured it out yet, you are here to serve a purpose. This work will help guide you to your most authentic self. An important part of the journey is understanding how the universe works. One principle states that what we put our attention on, our energy naturally follows. So, it's important to pay attention to your thoughts. For example, are you focused on not being depressed? Or do you focus on feeling alive and vibrant? If you focus your attention on what you don't want, i.e., being depressed or anxious, you will get more of what you don't want because that's where your attention is focused. Setting an intention will focus your attention on the outcome that you truly want. When you choose a point of focus, your mind finds ways to create that in your life. If you focus on how depressed you are and what's making you depressed, you'll get more of that. But if you set your intentions on feeling good, creating a life of wellness and vibrancy, your mind will find ways to create that. It's empowering to know I have choices about where to focus my attention and the choices I make bring the health and happiness I long for.

Gain Clarity and Discover Your Intentions Exercise

This sentence completion exercise is designed to explore the intention behind your desires. Take some time to really go within and think about what each sentence means to you. Take as much time as you need:

Before beginning, I invite you to breathe and focus on your heart space (the area around your heart). According to the Heart Math Institute, Heart-focused breathing is about directing your attention to the heart area and breathing a little more deeply than normal. Start by placing your hand over your heart as you breathe to direct your focus to your heart. As you breathe in, imagine you are doing so through your heart, and, as you breathe out, imagine it is through your heart. Do this 3 times. This will center you and allow space to receive the answers.

Complete the following sentences.

I want to overcome this problem because...

I am hoping that these solutions will give me...

Health and wellness are...

If I am more healthy, vibrant and alive, then I will...

The real reasons that I want to be healthy are...

Ultimately, health will allow me to...

When I practice self-care, it makes me feel...

11

Soul empowered means…

Now that you invested the time to complete these sentences, what insights, understanding or 'ah ha' moments did you experience? Don't skip this step. It is a very important and crucial step for making your dreams come true and living your soul's purpose and a powerful life. Anyone can pick up a book, but not everyone follows through. In fact, it's believed that only 20% of people who pick up a self-help book read the entire book and follow the instructions. The other 80% of readers never get past the first couple of pages.

Now that you know your why and have identified your intentions, it's time to set that vision in motion. Our minds see in pictures. When you create a vision, look at it on a daily basis, and feel what it would be like to manifest your vision, it intensifies your goal and sets things in motion more quickly. I invite you to create a vision board. If you're new to vision boards, I'll explain what you need and how to create one.

What you'll need

Poster board
Glue/glue sticks
Magazines or online access to images, quotes, and words of inspiration
Markers, colored pencils or crayons
Scissors
Your creative, childlike imagination

Start with finding images, quotes, and pictures that represent what you want to create. Browse through magazines or online. Recall your whys and your intentions. What will this look like when you have it? How will you know? How will you feel? Find all the pictures that represent your new life. Don't censor. There is no right or wrong here. This is your process. Trust yourself and trust your process. Dream big. Focus on what you want. The answers are within, ready to reveal themselves.

Now, cut or print out all the pictures, images, words and phrases that represent your vision and glue them to the poster board. Make a collage. Place the images, photos, and words in whatever way feels good for you. And don't forget to have fun with it!

When you're done, hang your vision board where you can see it every day. Invest the time to look at your vision board. Take a "selfie" of you vision board so that you have it with you to look at throughout the day. Remember the FEELING that you want to create, even if you're not there yet.

Sally loved this process. It really helped her to create an image of what she wanted. Through this process, she recognized she wanted to feel calm and happy, so she found a picture of a woman with a smile on her face. She realized that she wanted to learn to eat healthy, so she chose pictures of healthy foods. She decided she wanted to ride her bike more, so she placed a picture of a bike and an athlete on her vision board. Next, she decided she wanted to learn to meditate, so she found a picture of someone meditating. She continued to find pictures of all the things she wanted to create. She hung this in her bedroom and spent 5 minutes each day looking at it and feeling what it would be like if she already had these things in her life.

I invite you to take a moment and really acknowledge yourself for being here and doing this work. Thank yourself for giving yourself this gift.

CHAPTER TWO

You Can Change Your Thoughts

Which Wolf Will Win?

One evening a Cherokee elder told his grandson about the battle that goes on inside people. He said, "My son, the battle is between the two 'wolves' that live inside us all. One is Unhappiness. It is fear, worry, anger, jealousy, sorrow, self-pity, resentment, and inferiority. The other is Happiness. It is joy, love, hope, serenity, kindness, generosity, truth, and compassion."

The grandson thought about it for a minute and then asked his grandfather, "Which wolf wins?"

The old Cherokee simply replied, "The one you feed."

I love this old fable. It really speaks truth about the thoughts we have and that we truly have the power to feed each side. We get to choose which side to feed.

Like a lot of people, Sally came to me with difficulty focusing. Her thoughts were running wild without discernment or consciousness. Many of her thoughts went unfiltered throughout the day. She absorbed negativity from her environment including friend's negativity, media and news outlets, work gossip, and other toxic energy. She couldn't understand how all of this made her feel unfocused and scattered or how it all contributed to her anxiety and depression.

Why is it so hard to focus on the present? The present moment is not something we're accustomed to being in. We've been conditioned to remember the past or focus on the future. We are consumed with thoughts and limiting beliefs we hold, stories we tell ourselves about our value and worth, messages received as children or throughout life. We are so busy thinking about things to do, things we should do or shouldn't do, and flooded with scare tactics by the media, it becomes difficult to weed through the noise. All of this causes us to become overwhelmed with anxiety and depression when we don't stop, breathe, and be present in order to make the distinction between our thoughts and the stimulation around us.

What Are You Focused On?

A penny for your thoughts. Are they helpful thoughts or harmful thoughts? You get what you focus on whether you want it or not. You may have heard that statement before. Are you focused on what's important? The things that REALLY matter? We have those areas in our lives that make a long-term impact on wellbeing, things like health, relationships, career and purpose, and spirituality. Are you focused on what you desire from the areas that matter most in your life? Or are you focused on fears, anxiety, what you don't have, what's wrong, and what you don't like? Are you gossiping about others, or judging and comparing yourself to others? These patterns may be just what are keeping you stuck.

Sally began to understand that the depression she was experiencing was caused by thoughts that were focused on the past. The anxiety she experienced was due to her focus on the future. She realized that she was holding onto the common misconception that we cannot control our thinking; our thinking controls us. How disempowering is that? The truth is YOU ARE NOT YOUR THOUGHTS. Did you know that you have 60,000 thoughts per day?! And of those thoughts, 95% of them are the same thoughts you had yesterday and to top it off, 80% of those thoughts are negative thoughts! Your thoughts are created by energy in the body and neural networks that are conditioned to think in certain ways because you've trained your brain to function that way. When we think in certain ways for years and years and years, our brain goes to that place automatically without much conscious effort. In fact, most thinking is done unconsciously. This is why most people tend to say they want to make a change, and then fail because their unconscious habits and thoughts get in the way.

Becoming Aware of Your Thoughts

Awareness is key when it comes to listening and paying attention to our thoughts, emotions and behavioral patterns. But what is awareness, really? Understanding that we are not our thoughts or emotions, but the observer of these. When we become the observer of our experiences, we can consciously pay attention to what we're thinking or feeling and begin to unravel the mystery behind it. We understand and see that thoughts may pop in our head, but we can begin to recognize that we do not have to buy into that thought. We can choose to think a different thought and decide to have a different experience.

Sally was amazed at how her thoughts were controlling her. As we moved forward with our sessions, we worked on developing conscious awareness and she began to uncover thoughts that she had no idea she was thinking! Thoughts happen so fast. Until we learn to slow

16

the mind down and create conscious awareness, we are victims of our unconscious minds. When we create conscious awareness in our lives we begin to open up and realize our true power. Sally excitedly embraced this concept. When we begin making conscious choices, we are no longer running on autopilot. Have you ever been driving in a car and arrived at your destination only to discover that you couldn't remember how you got there? When we live our lives in that way, our unconscious minds are automatically running our lives. We are more likely to react negatively to those around us. Without conscious awareness, we continue to be driven by unconscious negative thoughts and beliefs. As Sally began to pay attention to her thoughts, she became aware of how the experience felt in her mind and body. Conscious awareness is really key to paying close attention to the thoughts that come up and what might trigger those thoughts. When you become aware, that is when change begins to happen.

Sally began to go within. I invited her to create awareness by focusing on her breath and paying attention to her thoughts, emotions and bodily sensations. This was very difficult at first and seemed very unnatural to her. Like many people, she was conditioned to be externally focused. According to her, she didn't connect to her body at all and looking inside at first was very daunting and a little scary. Sally had difficulty staying focused. She experienced "monkey mind"; her thoughts jumped from thought to thought, all over the place, like a monkey jumping from branch to branch. This was the first time she was able to experience what it meant to look deep within and discover which thoughts were there to support her and which ones were holding her back.

Create Conscious Awareness Practices

1. Set the intention. By setting the intention that you choose to create conscious awareness, your brain will find ways to become aware.
2. Question your thoughts, beliefs, emotions, and patterns of behavior. We are all creatures of habit and you're likely doing

some things the way you've always done them. The question is, why? How is that impacting you? Is it keeping you stuck?

3. Become aware of the beauty that you have around you, the little things that you take for granted or don't typically think twice about; like your breath, the flowers blooming, or hitting every green light on your way to work.

4. Be mindful of the present moment. When you connect to your breath, you choose to slow down and focus inward. Your breath connects you to the present moment.

Creating Time for a Mindfulness/Meditation Practice

Sally was excited to begin a mindfulness practice. She recognized that by using this time for herself and learning to quiet her mind, she was setting the stage for her daily interactions. The time she invested in meditation carried over into being mindful in all of her daily interactions. This realization allowed her to be more in control and choose the thoughts that were helping her manage and even eliminate anxiety-provoking thoughts.

Starting a Mindfulness Practice

1. **A quiet environment**: Choose a quiet place in your home, office, garden, place of worship, or in the great outdoors where you can relax without distractions or interruptions.

2. **A comfortable position**: Get comfortable, sit up with your spine straight, either in a chair or on the floor. You can also try a cross-legged or lotus position.

3. **A point of focus**: With eyes open, cast downward, or closed, focus on your breathing, and just notice it without trying to change it.

4. **An observant, nonjudgmental attitude**: Don't worry about distracting thoughts that go through your mind or whether you're doing it "right". If thoughts come up during your mindfulness session, don't fight them. Instead, gently turn your attention back to your breath.

5. **Use a timer**: When you are first getting started, I recommend using a timer. This allows time to float by. At first, set the timer for 5 minutes. Work your way up to 20 or more minutes from there.

What Does Belief Have to Do With It?

Sally noticed that her unconscious thoughts and beliefs about herself and the world were causing her to feel "not good enough" or "not deserving enough." Limiting beliefs control our actions and behaviors, our thoughts and how we show up in the world. They're continually driving us until we uncover them and become aware. It's the coolest thing in the world when you change these thoughts and beliefs. In turn, this will completely change your life, as it did Sally's.

Once she began to uncover the limiting beliefs, Sally began to dispute them through awareness, self-compassion, and changing the overall energy she put behind the thoughts. Sally and I used this next exercise to get to the bottom of her limiting beliefs, the beliefs that were keeping her from moving forward and living the life she truly wanted for herself.

Uncovering Limiting Beliefs Exercise

Here is a short exercise that you can use to help uncover the limiting beliefs

1. Think of a specific thought or upsetting situation (pick one thing at this time and you can do others later).
2. Ask yourself what does this mean or say about me, about others or about the world?
3. Ask yourself again 2 or 3 times what does this say or mean about me and you will get to the core belief.
4. Find at least 3 examples of how this belief is NOT true.

Example:

Event: A friend doesn't return your phone call.

Questioning: What does this say or mean about me, about others, or about the world?

Thought: I don't think she likes me.

Questioning: What does this say or mean about me, about others, or about the world?

Thought: I am sure none of my other friends like me.

Questioning: What does this say or mean about me, about others, or about the world?

Limiting Belief: I am unlovable.

What are 3 examples of how this limiting belief is not true:

1. My friend threw me a birthday party.
2. My other friend took me out to lunch.
3. My sister calls me every week to say hi and tell me she's thinking of me.

Self-Compassion Comes First

What is self-compassion? Self-compassion can often times be the hardest concept to fully embrace. Many people struggle with this because we're taught that loving ourselves is narcissistic or selfish, but this is a myth that is embedded in our culture. According to Kristin Neff at selfcompasion.org, self-compassion means treating yourself the same way you would someone else when they are suffering. She explains, "it is noticing when others are suffering, being moved by that suffering so your heart responds to their pain and offering understanding and kindness to others when they fail or make mistakes." To love ourselves and show compassion for our humanness is to recognize that we need space for mistakes, too. We are usually our own worst critic and can be harder on ourselves than anyone else. What if we turned the compassion we have for others, toward ourselves? So, it was of the utmost importance that Sally and I worked on self-compassion. She noticed that she was always the hardest on herself and didn't allow herself the same flexibility and room for error as she did her friends and family. She noticed that her words were harshest to herself when she made a mistake and rarely cut herself any slack. We did the following exercise from Kristin Neff's self-compassion work:

1. First, think about times when a close friend felt really bad about him or herself or was really struggling in some way. How did you respond to your friend in this situation? Please write down what you typically do, what you say, and note the tone in which you typically talk to your friends.
2. Now think about times when you feel bad about yourself or are struggling. How do you typically respond to yourself in these situations? Please write down what you typically do, what you say, and note the tone in which you talk to yourself.
3. Did you notice a difference? If so, ask yourself why. What factors or fears come into play that lead you to treat yourself and others so differently?
4. Please write down how you think things might change if you responded to yourself in the same way you typically respond to a close friend when they're suffering.

What did you learn about yourself? If you're anything like Sally, you recognized that you treat your friends better than you treat yourself. This is common, and it's also something you can become aware of and change. What if you became your own best friend? How might things be different? Do you remember a time when you were motivated by beating yourself up? Probably not. You build your self-worth on identifying and embracing your strengths. I invite you to take the self-compassion road today. What does that look like for you? Compare that with the road you've been on. Which one is more pleasant and life-affirming?

Bringing In the Light

After teaching Sally about self-compassion, we worked on the power of light energy. Light has a strong and high vibrational frequency when brought into our bodies. We can use the light from source, universe, God, or whatever name feels right for you. When we activate light and consciously and intentionally bring it into our bodies, we move it into any darkness that may be present. It helps us connect with our soul and higher self when we connect to the light. It allows us to raise our vibration and move energy from a heavy energy to lightness. When we bring light into our bodies, we are bringing light into the world.

As Sally began to embrace this concept, I invited her to work with the light. She worked on bringing in the light by trying the following exercise:

I invite you to begin by settling into a comfortable position either sitting in a chair or on a cushion. Make any adjustments necessary and allow yourself to sink into your chair. If you choose to, please close your eyes and begin to look inward. I invite you to take three deep breaths.

Inhale through your nose, deep into your belly; exhale through your mouth, releasing any tension you may have. Feel the tension slipping away with each out breath. If you have any thoughts or distractions that keep you from being present in this moment, I invite you to put this thought or distraction in a bubble and imagine it floating as far away from you as possible until it is a speck of dust and then allow it to dissolve in front of you. If you need to do this several times, take the time and do this.

Take another breath. Inhale again, slowly. This time imagine peace and calm entering your body, filling your body with each breath. Breathe into your stomach and allow your breath to reach your toes, exhale through your mouth, feeling any stress you may have leave your body with the outbreath. Sink further and further into your chair.

Inhale one more time with intention. Inhale into your heart space and create a vision of the experience you would like to gain from this meditation. Is it renewed energy or relaxation? Acceptance of yourself? Love? Peace? Breathe that intention into your body and circulate it into your cells. Now, centered in the intention, exhale any remaining tension and envision it flowing into the center of the earth. When you are ready, return to your normal breathing, keeping the intention with you.

Now imagine a light shining from above your head, from source energy, Universe or God, or whatever you call it, flowing into your head, seeping into your head and brain, removing any darkness or spots of tension, resistance or discomfort. Imagine a well-lit area, open to receive the light. Relax each tension spot as the light moves through your entire being. Imagine this light seeping into your face, jaw, eyes, forehead, nose and mouth, dissolving any dark spots or areas of discomfort you see, making way to be light and open to possibilities, softening your body as it moves along. Now allow it to spread down your neck, shoulders, and arms, into your chest, penetrating your heart with light energy, through your abdomen, your back and down your spine. Immerse this light into all of your organs. Feel the light move into your cells, through the cell walls, into the center of the cell. Feel it in the very place that your energy comes from.

Imagine the beam of light as loving energy fueling your cells, the very cells that emanate your being. Allow this light to continue to move down through your hips, buttocks, pelvic area, spreading down your legs, through your feet. Allow the light to pass through your feet to the earth's center, to pick up the powerful grounding energy that earth has to offer. Allow the light to beam all the way back to you, coming up through your body again, cascading like a fountain of light out the top of your head.

Allow this light to create a bubble around your entire being. Allow that feeling to fill your whole body, lighting you up. Allow that feeling to spread throughout your whole body. Extend that feeling to 3 feet outside of you, lighting your path so that not only you feel the shift from within your being, others for miles around you sense a light energy beaming through you.

Now that you've spread the light through and around your body.... Feel your body as a whole. Set the intention to carry this feeling and light with you for the rest of the day. When you're ready, open your eyes.

Replacing Negative Thoughts with Love

Love is the highest vibration. When we think loving thoughts, express loving thoughts and feel those loving thoughts we raise our vibration and the vibration of others around us. Words have power. They create the feeling associated with your thought based on the words you choose to use. Thoughts can appear so quickly. When we consciously choose to think new thoughts, we begin to change our reality. In traditional Cognitive Behavioral Therapy, it is suggested that you stop negative thinking and interrupt your thought pattern by yelling the word STOP at your thoughts to make yourself stop thinking that thought. This can be so abrasive and harsh to yell at yourself. When did yelling get anyone to do anything productive and feel good? I invite you to say the word LOVE each time you catch yourself thinking an unhelpful or negative thought. Each time you say love, gently focus on the area around your heart. Send love to the person or situation you were thinking about. Each time you think negatively about yourself, say LOVE. When we show up and love what is rather than trying to push it away, the hold it has on us lessens and we begin to look through the eyes of love instead of fear. Each time you do this, you are training your brain to choose love and your neural pathways will strengthen in the vibration of love.

Affirmations on Fire

Using affirmations can be a powerful force. It is my experience that affirmations are most effective when paired with a strong emotion that connects the words with your physical being. Often times affirmations are just words you repeat over and over, hoping for results. The problem with saying typical affirmations, is your mind doesn't really believe what you're saying if there is no evidence to support it. Think about a time when you were angry. You can probably remember what your body felt like because your body remembers emotion. The same is true for happy occasions. In order for affirmations to be a powerful force, we need to focus on our emotional state by creating the feeling we want to experience.   For instance, most people may not have a positive experience with giving a speech in public because it causes a lot of anxiety. What if you were to create the feeling of having confidence ahead of time while stating your affirmation?

Let's Create Your Affirmation

1. Write out what you want to affirm.
2. Be clear and specific.
3. Use an I statement.
4. State it in the Positive.
5. State it in the Present.
6. Examples:

    - I am now confident in giving my speech.
    - I am loveable the way I am.
    - I exude love everywhere I go.
    - I am calm and centered today.
    - I look for the gift in every interaction.
    - I now find joy in all of my activities.

7. Take a moment and create your own or use one of the examples.

Now, think about a time when you felt confident. How did confidence feel (or loveable, or loving, or calmness, etc.) in your body?. Stand up and walk with confidence. Jump up and down and yell with strong emotion, "I am now confident in giving my speech." Visualize what your body feels like, looks like and you how you articulate your words. Make the image as big as you can and feel every part of your being as confident as you possibly can.

Can you feel the difference?

Too Old? Think Again!

Sally came to me when she was about 30 years old and thought she was too old to start making changes. She held the belief that "old

25

dogs can't learn new tricks." This is a great example of an old belief passed down. If you think you're too old to change your patterns and behaviors, think again! A new field of research called neuroplasticity is showing that your brain creates new neural pathways whenever you learn or do something new or think in a new way. Each time you behave in a different way or practice something new, the stronger the pathway becomes. We have the power to change the way we think about anything! Imagine what this means for your health, wealth and happiness!

Change the Meaning, Change Your Life

As Sally worked through her thoughts, she began to uncover some ideas and thoughts that she really wanted to question. She began to recognize that she gave certain meanings to her thoughts. In reality, the meaning she was giving the thoughts she had about different situations were making her feel bad about herself. She shared that she was upset with her boss because she didn't think she liked her. She didn't believe she belonged in her office and this made her timid and shy.
She didn't want to participate at work. She was always trying hard to succeed and prove herself. But she didn't feel good enough not matter how hard she tried. We worked on the meaning she was giving the situation with her boss.

We can change the meaning we give to each situation when we begin to create awareness and understand what we are holding onto and why. When we ask questions about what we're struggling with, it begins to open up new pathways so that different thoughts and beliefs emerge. For instance, changing the meaning of 'my boss must not like me' to 'my boss must be stressed because of demands on her time' changes the way you feel about yourself, your boss and the situation. We get to choose what we want to focus on and what we want it to mean to us. Let's begin thinking in a new way. Here are some questions to get you started. Ask yourself these questions routinely when faced with challenges and see what changes!

1.   What are you holding onto that is no longer serving you?
2.   What do you need to let go of?
3.   What story are you telling yourself?

4. What meaning are you giving your experiences?

Questions Create Answers

Sally noticed, through awareness, that she was asking herself all kinds of dis-empowering questions. And guess what kind of answers she was getting? Not empowering ones.

What answer might you get when you ask, "What is wrong with me?"' or "What else could go wrong?" or "Why do bad things always happen to me?" These types of questions keep you stuck in the past, in the problem, what's not working, why it won't work, what you don't like about yourself/the other person/the situation, and in blame. When we begin to make a conscious effort to choose life-affirming questions, our brains will automatically start to search life-affirming answers.

Power Questions to Move You

Here are some questions that are a great way to start and end your day and help move you through a challenge and begin creating freedom in your life.

Morning Power Questions

1. What am I happy about in my life now?
   What about that makes me happy?
   How does that make me feel?
2. What am I excited about in my life now?
   What about that makes me excited?
   How does that make me feel?
3. What am I proud about in my life now?
   What about that makes me proud?
   How does that make me feel?
4. What am I grateful for?
   What about that makes me grateful?
   How does that make me feel?

5. What am I enjoying in my life right now?
   What about that do I enjoy?
   How does that make me feel?
6. What am I committed to in my life right now?
   What about that makes me committed?
   How does that make me feel?
7. Who do I love? Who loves me?
   What about that makes me loving?
   How does that make me feel?

Evening Power Questions

1. What have I given today?
2. In what ways have I been a giver today?
3. What did I learn today?
4. How has today added to the quality of my life OR how can I use today as an investment in my future?

Problem Solving Questions

1. What is great about this problem?
2. What is not perfect yet?
3. What am I willing to do to make it the way I want it?
4. What am I willing no longer to do to make it the way I want it?
5. How can I enjoy the process while I do what is necessary to make it the way I want it?

Power Questions adapted from Tony Robbins

CHAPTER THREE

Your Emotions Give Your Soul Power

"Each time you meet an old emotional pattern with presence, your awakening to truth can deepen. There's less identification with the self in the story and more ability to rest in the awareness that is witnessing what's happening. You become more able to abide in compassion, to remember and trust your true home. Rather than cycling repetitively through old conditioning, you are actually spiraling toward freedom." ~Tara Brach, True Refuge: Finding Peace and Freedom in Your Own Awakened Heart

Emotions Make Us Human

When Sally came to me, she was unaware of how her emotional experiences impacted her internal life. She was looking outside of herself for answers and had never really looked within to trust that she knew what was best for her. She relied on other people to tell her what was right or wrong. She didn't know or see how the environment and people she relied upon affected her wellbeing. As with most people, she wasn't taught to look within for her voice or for the answers to healing. She was disconnected from her emotions and who she was as a person. Through

29

our work together she discovered that healing and emotions are a part of life and she learned to validate her own emotions through self-love and compassion.

Emotions are what sets humans apart from other species. Often times, we get so caught up in the fear of looking within because we're afraid to feel the full range of deep emotions, including joy, anger, confidence, or sadness. By staying small with our emotions, we learn that being externally focused is a way of getting through life. It's easier to look outside of ourselves for the answers to life's questions than it is to look within and discover who we really are at a soul level. It's easy to think everyone else has it all figured out. It's safer to look to others because then we think we won't make mistakes or get it wrong or we have someone else to blame. But here's the thing…you are giving your power away every time you look to someone else for validation or for how to live your life or for how to feel. You are losing the power that comes from what your soul is meant to do in this life. But it's not your fault. If you haven't learned to look inward, it's most likely that you didn't receive this lesson from your parents or caregivers. A lot of people struggle with looking inward because it can be scary. When you begin to quiet your emotions and learn to listen to their messages, real answers begin to emerge. Your truth begins to emerge. I've heard from many clients that they'd rather die than face their negative emotions. Now, that may seem extreme, but for a lot of people their suffering is deep and dark. We've been taught to invalidate our own emotional experiences.

Sally grew up in a good home, with loving parents who had good intentions. Like their parents, they were not taught about emotions and their importance for living an emotionally healthy life. Recognizing that our parents were not perfect, did their best and gave only what they had available to give is an important first step. If they weren't taught about emotions or received validation or were unaware, that's the knowledge (or lack of knowledge) and experience they passed on to their children. Sally was taught to push her emotions down and she didn't learn how to process them. She didn't understand that she has more control over her emotions than she was lead to believe. But like many of us, she was taught to place more value in putting on a happy face at all times. She was taught that she should cry alone, and anger is scary and should be stifled. She learned to fear emotional experiences. She was given the messages and repeatedly told, "you shouldn't feel like that" or "don't be so angry" or "you don't have it that bad" or "big girls don't cry". Any of these statements are invalidating and will cause you to fear or disregard the most beautiful human experiences.

Sally expressed to me during a session that she felt like she would be happy when her partner was nice to her and listened and she could be happy once she got promoted. We discussed how this is an easy trap to fall into because there's always going to be the next thing to look forward to and want in order to "be happy." It's easy to get sidetracked with things that we believe will make us "happy." You know, those things like the perfect job, the perfect relationship, the perfect body, the car, the house, the boat... fill in the blank. We are trying to attain these things because we feel like they will satisfy that need in some way. We feel like they will be the ticket item that makes us happy and gives us that *thing* we've been missing all along. What happens when you receive that job or relationship? Does it miraculously make you happy? Perhaps, in the short-term. But in the long-term it is just another Band-Aid to satisfy a deeper, unfulfilled desire. What is the deep longing? What is the emotional connection to the material thing that we hope to gain? What feeling are you trying to feel? As Sally and I explored this concept, she began to realize that she deeply wanted the sense of freedom in her life. She needed to feel like she had enough money to be financially independent and wanted her partner to hear what she was saying because she felt so stifled.

When we begin to really dive deep and look within ourselves and remember our wholeness, then we can start to uncover the layers of emotions that keep us from being true to ourselves. We begin to live by our values and honor all parts of ourselves.

When you are able to feel a full range of emotional experiences, it allows you to express yourself and experience what your soul wants you to feel. It is my belief that when we decided to embark on this human experience, we did so with the desire to feel the full range of human emotions--pain, joy, love, sadness, and anger. These emotions allow us to fully connect to our soul and the spiritual growth we are seeking. We

31

wanted all of these human experiences because our spirit form isn't able to experience them.

What would life be without joy or anger? Anger is your soul's way of saying, "This isn't right, I need to do something different" or "My values have been violated and I need to choose another path". When feelings go unexpressed, they become stacked like layers of an onion until we are willing to look at and feel each layer. Feelings continue to stack until it becomes unbearable and life becomes hard because we haven't stopped to feel our experiences. We are working against our soul purpose and life feels like a big struggle. If you feel hurt and don't acknowledge the hurt, it may turn to sadness and sadness may turn to anger and anger may turn to rage, until depression or anxiety ensues or other dis-ease manifests.

Working with Sally to help her acknowledge her emotions, I noticed she was able to see how her lifetime of emotions became stacked, creating a short fuse, high anxiety and depression was always present. Using the analogy of holding a beach ball underwater, I asked her to imagine holding it down for hours, days, and years. I explained that eventually she'll get tired of holding down all that pressure under water and the beach ball will pop up out of the water. She won't be able to control it. I explained that it's the same with emotions. If she doesn't listen to, honor, and express them in a healthy way they will erupt in unhealthy ways. This made sense to Sally. She told me that she found herself getting angry at other drivers or she lashed out at her loved ones or the barista for things that seemed small. She began to make the connection between unprocessed emotions and health problems, including low thyroid numbers. She began to realize that the emotional and physical dis-ease were the symptoms of her deep and uncharted pain.

Let's take a deeper look at the layers of emotions. I asked Sally to think about the mind as an iceberg, with only about 5% available to her conscious awareness in day-to-day life, like when she's choosing to go to work or eating her breakfast, etc. The remaining 95% under the surface is what's really running the show. This is the unconscious mind that drives behaviors including overeating or not going for that promotion at work. It's why you do what you do and includes the fears and limiting beliefs that keep you stuck. These may stem from childhood, past relationships, media, friends, and what you've learned along the way. These are the messages you received and believed about what you deserve or don't deserve, or whether you are worthy or unworthy.

I began to help Sally connect to her body through awareness and scanning her body for emotions and sensations she was feeling. This was an important step to tuning in and beginning to listen to the underlying messages her soul was sending.

We continued to incorporate the body scan into our sessions and she continued to practice at home, as well.

I invite you to try this and make it a part of your day.

Body Awareness Scan

It might be helpful to have a friend or partner read this script for you or record it on your phone or another device and listen to it. You can also find pre-recorded body scan meditations online.

Begin by getting into a comfortable position. Sit in a chair and allow your back to be straight, but not stiff, with your feet on the ground. You could also do this practice standing or if you prefer, you can lie down with your head supported. Your hands could be resting in your lap or at your side. Gently close your eyes. Take a deep breath in and breathe out long and slow. Breathe in through your nose and out through your nose or mouth. Feel your stomach expand on an inhale and relax and let go as you exhale. Feel yourself being fully supported by whatever your sitting, lying or standing on. Begin to shift your attention from outside to inside yourself. If you are distracted by sounds in the room, simply notice this and bring your focus back to your breathing.

Slowly focus your attention on the scalp, head, jaw and face. Just notice what is there. Is there any tension or areas of discomfort? If you notice anything, just breathe into it. Continue to breathe and shift focus down to the neck, shoulder and throat. We tend to hold a lot of tension

33

I these areas, so take a moment and just be with the sensations, tightness, pain or other discomfort. As you breathe, imagine feeling tension falling off your shoulders. Observe all of the sensations. Notice the movement of the air as you breathe into or out of the nostrils or mouth. As you exhale, notice your muscles relaxing and letting go of any tension you may be holding on to.

On the next outbreath, shift the focus and bring your awareness down to your arms. Observe the sensations, if any, that may be occurring there. You might notice some difference between the left arm and the right arm. Just gently notice without judgement.

As you continue to breathe, bring your awareness to your chest and heart area and observe your heart as it rhythmically beats. Notice how your chest rises and falls with each breath. Let go of any thoughts that may arise. On the next outbreath, shift the focus to your hands and fingers. Take a moment and just breathe into this area and breathe out as if you are letting go what is no longer serving you. You are letting go.

Slowly move your attention up to your mid and upper back. What do you notice? If you feel any tension, invite the tension to soften with each outbreath. Gradually move your focus to your stomach area. Notice your belly rising or falling with each breath. If you notice any thoughts or sensations that happen in the stomach area, just notice them, gently take a deep breath into this area and breathe out any feelings of discomfort.

Slowly move to the sensations in your lower back and pelvis area. A lot of tension can build here, just observe any tension or feelings without judgement. If any thoughts arise just allow your attention to shift gently back to this area. Breathe deeply into this area and breathe out anything you notice here.

Move your energy to your legs. Breathe into and out of the legs. Then on the next out breath, allow the legs to dissolve in your mind. If you notice any discomfort, pain or stiffness, simply notice it without judgement. Open up your awareness to allow your attention to move down to your thighs, knees, calves, and ankles. Observe all of the sensations you are experiencing throughout the entirety of your legs.

Move your awareness to your feet. What do you notice? Are they tired, cold, warm, ready for action? Observe any sensations and take a breath right into your feet.

Allow your awareness to move back up each body part and again breathe into that area, if you notice any discomfort. Notice your body as a whole and thank yourself for giving yourself the time to do this practice. Breathe deeply. When you are ready, open your eyes and return your attention to the present moment.

The more you tune into your body in this way, the more you will begin to learn the cues it is sending you and you will learn to trust those cues. Being in tune with your body, mind and spirit will allow you to open up to the power of your soul's truth.

Sally did a lot of work that helped her recognize that emotions are neither good nor bad. They just are. She learned that it's the meaning that she gives to them that makes all the difference in the world. I gave her the example of two men driving separately down the road when they come upon traffic that's backed up by a train that isn't moving. I explained that both men have somewhere to be and are now running late. The first guy is yelling at the train, which obviously isn't going to move just because he's yelling. The other guy takes this opportunity to chill, turn up the music, jam out, focus on what is within his control, and just enjoy the moment. Who do you think is going to get through the experience with more energy and a better mood? Each man has the identical experience that is out of their control. But the meaning they both gave it and what they do with the experience was completely different.

Sally grew up believing she needed to be strong. Like many people, she learned to equate strength with not feeling sad or vulnerable. She learned that she would be perceived as weak if she showed any vulnerability. She was inadvertently taught that she shouldn't show her feelings. She recalled a time of major transition in her life when she was

15 when she lost someone very close to her and instead of feeling the sadness, fear, and grief, she believed she had to "be strong" for her siblings. But that came at a price. She began acting out in other ways. She went from being a straight A student to dropping out of high school. She took her anger out on herself and became self-destructive. She processed the loss in her life in unhealthy ways. If she was vulnerable or showed fear as a child, she was told to go to her room or that "big girls don't cry" and all of these messages reinforced the belief that it wasn't okay to show her pain. She didn't have the tools to manage or even begin to understand what was happening. Her unconscious mind was taking over and it continued to control her until she became aware of the path she was on and wanted to make changes.

As Sally and I continued to work together, I shared with her the value of vulnerability. I shared with her the wisdom of Brene Brown's book, *Daring Greatly*. Ms. Brown writes, "vulnerability is not weakness, and the uncertainty, risk, and emotional exposure we face every day are not optional. Our only choice is a question of engagement. Our willingness to own and engage with our vulnerability determines the depth of our courage and the clarity of our purpose; the level to which we protect ourselves from being vulnerable is a measure of our fear and disconnection." Sally resonated with this and recognized that it was more empowering to show up and use her voice by sharing her feelings and using the intuitive wisdom of her inner truth and speaking that to the world. She knew she had a message to share, she just had to uncover it through the inner work.

As Sally and I continued to work through her beliefs about emotions, I explained that emotions are like children. Like all little children, they want to be seen and heard. They want you to pay attention to them. What happens when a child isn't given love and attention? They start misbehaving and acting out. When you become aware and begin paying attention to your emotional experiences and give them the attention they need and deserve, your emotions begin quieting down. Even though the past is the past, your "emotional children" will continue to seem uncontrollable for as long as you choose to ignore them or stuff them. As an adult, you have control over how you choose to respond and validate your own emotional experience. Emotion is "energy in motion". When we experience an emotion, there's a chemical reaction that occurs. It is just a neutral circuit of energy; energy moving through our bodies. When we give an emotion a name or meaning, like "anger" or "sadness," it perpetuates itself, takes on a life of its own and grows. That energy in motion needs about 90 seconds to be felt and acknowledged. Then it is released from our bodies. When we take the time to feel and acknowledge our emotional experience, without judgement, we begin to heal.

Sally began to realize and understand that showing vulnerability gave her strength to be the most authentic person she could be. When she showed vulnerability it allowed her to express her emotions and to feel the flow of emotional freedom. She was no longer trapped by her unprocessed emotions!

Learning to acknowledge and express your emotions is one of the most freeing and liberating experiences you can have. When you learn to fully express yourself and all your emotions in healthy ways, you release the chains that keep you hidden, that keep you stuck in your past. When you grasp this wholeheartedly, you awaken to who you are meant to be. What would that feel like for you?

Sally began to embrace this concept and saw that her emotions are patterns or chemical reactions to past events. Her body remembered what it felt like in the past when events occurred that produced strong emotional responses that she was unable to process. Her body was doing a great job of trying to keep her safe from ever feeling that pain again. We discussed how the painful emotions she experienced in the past is just that: The past. When a stressful event occurred in the past, her body went into a fight, flight or freeze mode. When something happened in the present that her body associated with an event from the past, it triggered an unconscious emotional response. When we experience a trauma, our body remembers. It doesn't matter how big or small, if we perceive it as a threat, it is a trauma. This becomes stored in our cellular memories or energy body, until we consciously look at it and safely release the energy in motion. We become triggered by an event in the present based on the past. Our body remembers certain cues in the environment through our senses. It can happen so quickly that we are not even aware of this. Certain smells, sounds, sights, tastes, or touches can trigger the same emotional response we had in the past. Our body will respond by fighting (getting defensive or angry), by flighting or fleeing (running away/avoiding) or freezing (feeling numb, stuck or unable to move).

According to Joe Dispenza, in his book, *Becoming Supernatural*, the long term-effects of unresolved survival emotions, such as the stress response to traumatic events, place the entire body into incoherence, setting the stage for stress induced health challenges. He goes on to say that these survival emotions draw from the energy field around your body creating a feeling of separation from coherence because your focus is on your body, time, the environment and the source of the problem. According to HeartMath Institute research on heart intelligence and accessing intuitive insight the heart can be either coherent or incoherent. They concluded when you are in coherence, "your life can be so much better than when you are incoherent." So, what does this mean? They go on to say, "Coherence is the state when the heart, mind, and emotions are in energetic alignment and cooperation. It is the state that builds resiliency, personal energy is accumulated, not wasted- leaving more energy to manifest intentions and harmonious outcomes."

Sally discussed with me an argument with her partner during which she felt like she was not being heard. Her partner wasn't listening and didn't want to hear what she was saying. She responded by getting angry and then shutting down for the rest of the night. We processed this and discussed emotional patterns. Feeling like she is not being heard is a strong belief she has and her partner was mirroring this belief for her. She recalled many times in her upbringing when she didn't feel heard and felt invalidated for her ideas, thoughts and creative expression. She was given the message that her voice was not important. In other words, her partner was playing a role in her life: Through his behavior, he activated this strong belief held in her body and cellular memory. His behavior was awakening this energy within her and was offering her an opportunity to process and heal this pattern. Once she learned to heal this pattern, she could then learn to approach the situation from a grounded place, rather than from her the old memory stored in her cells.

Our lives are filled with lots of patterns. We have thought patterns, behavioral patterns and emotional patterns. One of Sally's emotional patterns was to get angry and then shut down emotionally. This is how her mind and body learned to protect her and keep her safe. Think about an upsetting situation in your life that you recently experienced. How did you respond to it? Did you respond in the typical way that you normally would? What was your emotional response? Did you get angry? Sad? Frustrated? Did you respond in the same way you typically do? What does your body do when you are sad? Or angry? Your physiology plays a huge role in how you feel. When your facial expression makes the same scrunched up look when you're angry, your body automatically goes into that anger mode. How do you respond when you're sad? Do you begin to get down on yourself, veg out in front of the TV with a glass of wine to distract yourself? This is a pattern. Does it feel like you're solving any problem with it? Probably not. Often times, we use distractions to keep ourselves from feeling what is painful and this continues the cycle of emotional patterns. Those distractions can come in for the form of television, foods, shopping, alcohol, drugs, gossiping or focusing on other people's problems.

When we begin to dive deep and look within ourselves we start to uncover the layers of emotions that keep us from being true to ourselves. We learn to remember that we are whole. We begin to live by our values and honor all parts of ourselves. I invite you to look at the layers of your emotions. You can do that digging deeper into your emotional experience. You've learned to create awareness of your breath, do a body scan and pay attention to your thoughts. Now, I offer you a mindful of emotions practice:

Mindful of Emotions Practice

Create a quiet space and bring your attention to your breath. Take 3 deep breaths by inhaling through your nose and exhaling through your mouth. Allow your breath to go back to normal and just notice it, as you breathe without trying to change anything. Tune into your body and just notice any sensations. Slowly scan your body from head to toe.

Notice any feelings that you are experiencing.

- Name the emotion.
- What word best describes what you are feeling?

Become curious about the emotion.

- How strong is the emotion?
- What do you notice in your body?
- Where are you feeling the emotion?
- Do you notice any tension or areas of discomfort?
- What is your body posture like?
- How are you breathing?
- What else do you notice?

Allow and accept the emotion.

- Remember, emotions are just energy in motion and they're only meant to last 90 seconds or less in your body. Emotions are normal body reactions to information in the environment.
- Take a moment and practice observing the emotion without judgment or trying to change it in any way.
- Allow it to move through you, as energy.
- If you notice yourself resisting or struggling against it, just notice that and shift to allowing the emotion to flow through you. Remember, you're safe.
- If any thoughts arise, just notice them and bring your attention back to your breath and the physical sensations in your body.

A Word About Forgiveness

Even though Sally had a good childhood, she didn't go unscathed. She experienced loss, rejection and pain. She shared experiences of losing her family members at a young age. We discussed how this had affected her and she realized she was holding onto resentments from 20 years before! We discussed how this felt in her body. She could still feel the pain of the incident. She had a lot of forgiving to do because of the loss. She began to understand that holding grudges or resentments toward another person or experience kept her from moving forward in life. Resentments hold us back because the negative energy is held in our body and keep us stuck in the past. They keep us from living our lives fully and embracing our present and future. When you hold on to resentment, it's like feeding yourself poison. You are the one that is suffering, not the other person. They may have wronged you, but they will not suffer just because you hold resentment toward them. They have their own life path to follow.

Each experience that we have is a learning opportunity for our soul's growth. Often times we don't consciously know the reason for the experiences we have in this life. Remember, it's the meaning we give to our experiences that either chains us or frees us. What if that person came into your life to teach you about letting go and forgiving? What would happen if you took a moment to forgive and let go? How freeing would that be? How does it feel in your body to live with those resentments? Does it feel constricting? Does it feel heavy? We are not victims of our circumstances. We are empowered souls with the capacity to choose our responses in every interaction. Sally began to understand that she has the ability to choose the meaning she gives to each situation. Even though it can be hard to believe at times, most things don't just happen to us; we create our life experiences. When life happens, how do you want to perceive that event? As a torturous life event or as a gift and teachable moment? When you let go of the victim mentality and take control of your life's destiny, your life path begins to open up. Letting go means lightening the load for the future.

The Power of Gratitude

Sally and I talked about the power of gratitude. This was not something she thought of before. She was confused about being grateful for her breath and for what she had, because she had just taken these things for granted. As we explored gratitude, she realized that having gratitude means appreciating what she has. Expressing gratitude began to have a major effect on her and her life. For one, she became aware that gratitude and stress can't live in the same space! So, she began to incorporate gratitude practices into her day when she was feeling stressed or depressed. Doing this had such an influence on her life, she began to do it as a daily practice. She didn't feel so stressed anymore. I introduced the concept of "where you put you focus, your energy will follow". When we focus on gratitude and the things that we appreciate about life, life will begin to change. Sally began to feel so different once she opened up her heart to gratitude. Her mind, body and relationships began to flourish!

Robert Emmons, the world's leading scientific expert on gratitude, reveals why gratitude is good for our bodies, our minds, and our relationships. He did a series of studies on gratitude and discovered by keeping a "gratitude journal" in which test subjects regularly recorded the things for which they were grateful, he found surprising results. Out of the one thousand people he studied, from ages 8 to 80, he found that people who practice gratitude consistently report a host of physical, psychological and social benefits including:

Physical
- Stronger immune systems.
- Less bothered by aches and pains.
- Lower blood pressure.
- Exercise more and take better care of their health.
- Sleep longer and feel more refreshed upon waking.

Psychological
- Higher levels of positive emotions.
- More alert, alive, and awake.
- More joy and pleasure.
- More optimism and happiness.

Social
- More helpful, generous, and compassionate.
- More forgiving.
- More outgoing.
- Feel less lonely and isolated.

42

When you look for things to be grateful for, more things will appear to be grateful for because your perception changes. When you change your mind, your world changes. When's the last time you felt grateful for what you have? Gratitude is an emotion that brings only wonderful things to you and your life.

Six Ways to Practice Gratitude Today

Journal About Gratitude

What are you grateful for in your life? Take a few minutes every evening to write down at least five good things about your day. The entries don't have to be major events—they might be as simple as a having dinner with your family, a sunny day, going for a walk or connecting with your breath. Remember to include yourself in your gratitude practice! Emmons suggests asking yourself these questions to invoke a deeper meaning of your gratitude practice and life:

1. Who or what inspired me today?
2. What brought me happiness today?
3. What brought me comfort and deep peace today?

Write a Letter of Gratitude

Who in your life would you like to thank? Who has graced your life with their presence? Think about someone who you would like to thank, or someone who you appreciate having in your life. Write a letter to them about what you appreciate about them, and send it off to them.

Visit Someone Who You Appreciate

Visit someone and tell them in person all the reasons you appreciate them. How have they made your life better; how have they added to the quality of your life?

Say "Thank You". Keep your eyes open throughout the day for reasons to say "thanks". Try to recognize the small actions people do every day that might be overlooked, such as a colleague who always goes the extra mile, or a friend who always seems willing to listen.

Take a Gratitude Walk

Go for a walk and take it all in. Feel what is around you and appreciate your surroundings. Experience the smell of flowers, a beautiful landscape, children laughing or a soothing breeze. Spend a few minutes focusing on each of your senses (sight, hearing, taste, smell, and touch) to find new things you may not have noticed.

Self-appreciation

Don't forget to include yourself in your gratitude practices. What is special and unique about you? Often times, we don't think in these terms, but when we begin to look inward and appreciate ourselves, we show up and allow our lights to shine. Give yourself the recognition. What are you grateful for today within yourself? How did you show up for yourself today? What did you do today?

Take Your Gratitude Practice One Step Further

As Sally began finding gratitude in her life by working with these exercises, I invited her to connect with the feeling of gratitude through her heart space. The heart space is the energetic area around your heart. When you connect with this area and begin to open up to the energy of the heart, your mind, emotions and body begin to work together in coherence. You stay in connection with your feelings and open up to your inner guidance.

According to the Heart Math Institute, consciously generating feelings of appreciation and gratitude while focusing and breathing through the area of the heart can offer much more coherence between the brain and heart and shift from a stressful place to an appreciative one. Take a moment during your gratitude practice and try the following exercise:

1. Focus on your heart area.
2. Take 3 deep breaths into your heart space.
3. Think of something or someone you are grateful for.
4. Stay in this space for several moments.
5. Feel the shift!

Clearing Emotional Disruptions in Your Energy System
Emotional Freedom Techniques (EFT/Tapping)

The next thing I taught Sally was EFT/Tapping. I taught her how EFT/Tapping worked with her body's energy system. The energy of emotion continues to cycle through our bodies until we notice the emotion and take steps to neutralize the emotional charge. When you have a strong emotion such as fear, sadness, or anger, and don't acknowledge it this causes a disruption in your energy system and creates an imbalance. According to Traditional Chinese Medicine, we all have meridians (or energy channels) in our bodies that allow vital energy to flow through 12 major organs. When we experience a stressful event or trauma, it causes a disruption in the energy system and energy stops flowing efficiently. For instance, the trigger of the Sally's partner not listening and Sally feeling that urge to get angry and shut down is a disruption in her energy system. That past event triggered her strong reaction each time she didn't feel heard. When we tune into what is upsetting us, while tapping on the meridian end points, we move the energy because emotion is energy in motion. When we become aware of it, listen to it, and pay attention to it, we are then empowered to move that energy through us.

See picture below (figure 1) for the meridian end-points.

Figure 1

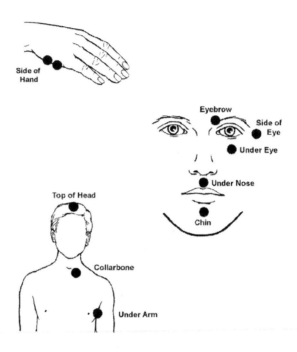

First, I asked Sally what issue she would like to work on. She reported the anxiety she feels when not being heard by her partner. I asked her what emotion comes up for her, and she reported anger. I asked her where she felt that in her body and she stated in her stomach. I asked her to rate the intensity of the feeling on a SUD scale (subjective units of distress scale) of 0 to 10, ten being the most intense. She identified it to be the number 8.

Next, I invited her to start tapping on the Side of Hand point and continue these steps:

46

- Side of Hand point: Begin tapping on the side of your hand (the fleshy part of your hand) and repeat the set-up phrase (include your own emotion):

- Even though I am feeling this __*Emotion*___ I love and accept myself (Repeat this phrase 3 times while tapping on the Side of Hand)

  o Sally's Example: *Even though I am feeling this* **anger in my stomach when I think about my partner not listening to me**, *I love and accept myself* (Repeat this phrase 3 times while tapping on the Side of Hand)

- Come up with a shortened version of the above phrase, for example "feeling angry." (include your emotion).

- Tap on each of the next points at least 5 to 7 times before moving on to the next point while repeating the reminder phrase (refer to the picture above for the tapping points).

- Eyebrow point (repeat "this anger")

- Side of eye point (repeat "this anger")

- Under eye point (repeat "this anger")

- Under nose point (repeat "this anger")

- Chin point (repeat "this anger")

- Collar bone point (repeat "this anger")

- Under arm point (repeat "this anger")

- Top of head point (repeat "this anger")

Sally and I tapped on "this anger" for 3 rounds. I assessed her SUDS scale and she reported feeling a level 3 anger. We then did a second round with "this remaining anger"

- Side of Hand point- Begin tapping on the side of your hand and repeat the set-up phrase and add your own feeling

- Even though I am feeling this ___*remaining feeling*___ I love and accept myself (Repeat this phrase 3 times while tapping on the Side of Hand)
  - o Sally's Example: *Even though I am feeling this* **remaining anger in my stomach when I think about my partner not listening to me**, *I love and accept myself* (Repeat this phrase 3 times while tapping on the Side of Hand)

- Come up with your reminder phrase, this is a shortened version of your set-up phrase, for example you can say "remaining angry." Or whatever you are feeling.

- Tap on each of the next points at least 5 to 7 times before moving onto the next point while repeating the reminder phrase (refer to the above picture for the tapping points).

- Eyebrow point (repeat "this remaining anger")

- Side of eye point (repeat "this remaining anger")

- Under eye point (repeat "this remaining anger")

- Under nose point (repeat "this remaining anger")

- Chin point (repeat "this remaining anger")

- Collar bone point (repeat "this remaining anger")

- Under arm point (repeat "this remaining anger")

- Top of head point (repeat "this remaining anger")

Tap each point and continue to do rounds of tapping until you get to a SUD of 0.

Tap in the Positive Resource

The next thing I showed Sally was called bi-lateral stimulation for increasing her good feelings. Bi-lateral stimulation is traditionally used in Eye Movement Desensitization and Reprocessing (EMDR). Bi-lateral stimulation is alternating stimulation in a rhythmic pattern using audio, tactile, visual cues while processing difficult memories or installing positive resources. During our sessions, Sally and I utilized this therapy for processing some of her more difficult beliefs and memories. I would recommend a trained EMDR therapist for this type of therapy. For the purpose of this book, I show you how to "tap in" positive feelings.

Creating a Resource State

1. Picture a time when you did something extraordinarily well. Using all your senses and feeling it in your body, remember how it felt. Sally really wanted to feel free since this was important to her and we discussed how she could choose to feel free now, rather than wait until "someday." She remembered what it was like when she lived on her own and was choosing to live life on her terms. She was in school, doing yoga, and just happy where she was.

2. Enhance all of the feelings, images, sights, sounds, smells, tastes of what it was like at that time in your life. Sally brought up how freedom felt in her body. She remembered learning to step into her own choices and path and brought this up to a level 8 in her body. When it was a level 8 in her body, I asked her to imagine a temperature knob in front of her that she could use to turn up her good feelings. I asked her to imagine turning the knob up as high as it could go. She turned the knob until it reached a level 10. This increased the intensity of her feelings.

3. As soon as the images, sounds, and feelings are clear and strong, imagine a circle on the floor. Imagine a symbol for the circle and give the circle a word that helps to activate it, i.e. success, peace, love and hold all the feelings and memories connected to the time you recall. Sally imagined a bird as her symbol, as this represented freedom for her and then named the circle "freedom."

4. Take a deep breath and step into the circle. Stand inside the circle and continue to intensify the memory.

5. Enhance the image with bi-lateral stimulation while standing in the circle. Bi-lateral stimulation is alternating taps or other stimulus on both sides of the body. For instance, you can either tap on both legs, alternating left-right-left-right. You may also do what is called the butterfly hug by crossing your arms, as if to give yourself a hug. The opposite hand touches the opposite shoulder (left hand touches right shoulder, right hand touches left shoulder), and alternate left-right. Tap for 30 seconds, stop and continue to enhance the image.

6. Continue to tap until you feel like you are at the heightened state of your positive resource.

Take some time with these exercises. Your emotions have been there for years and it takes time to heal. Love yourself through this process and find gratitude in your heart space for the wonderful work you are doing.

CHAPTER FOUR

Food Creates Mood

Let food be thy medicine, thy medicine shall be thy food. ~Hippocrates

When Sally came to me, she was eating a typical Standard American Diet (SAD). She rarely ate breakfast and drank at least 3 large mugs of coffee with loads of sugar. For lunch she had leftover pizza, takeout, drive-through fast food, and lots of chips. She reported a craving for salty foods. She would typically eat late at night and swallow her food down with a beer or glass of wine. She felt completely disconnected from her body. One of the things Sally and I worked on included educating her about what we feed our bodies nutritionally is just as important as our thoughts, emotions and the environment in which we live. Feeding our bodies, mind and soul helps improve clarity and focus, and affects our mood.

As a psychotherapist and wellness coach, it is important for me to look at the whole person, not just a part of the person. If food is taken into the body from processed, nutritionally deficient sources, it's going to affect the way a person feels including decreasing motivation to overcome anxiety or depression. It also creates a disconnect from the soul and being all they can be. In fact, it will contribute to anxiety and depression. We cannot live a high vibrational life when we consume low vibrational foods. Studies now show there is a direct link to the food we eat and how we feel. Let's take a deeper look.

What goes into the body, affects the mind. Everything is energy, including the food we eat. All the food that we eat has an energetic component, a vibration. Some food has a higher vibration. The old adage is correct when it says, "we are what we eat." We become the energy that is within that energetic make up of food. According to Anthony Robbins in his Living Health program, our bodies require a certain frequency to be alive and live optimally. This can be measured through megahertz of energy or MHz. Your body requires a range of 60-70 MHz to function at its best. This is what gives you your lifeforce energy, chi, prana or spirit as it is often referred to. Anything less than 60-70 MHz begins to reduce our ability to function and dis-ease is often the result. As a reference point, cancer operates at 42 MHz.

Think about when you eat chocolate cake, how much energy do you think is in that food? Take a guess… If you guessed 0 MHz, you would be correct! How do you feel physically, emotionally or spiritually after you eat that food? That may clue you into why these foods are so depleting on your energy system; they are devoid of energy. Now think about how eating that for years and years without paying attention to how it affects your body. When you feed your body non-nutritional substances that have no benefit at all, this wreaks havoc on your cellular health. When you are operating at anything less than the 60-70 MHz, it shows up as addictions, anger, and confusion as well as depression, anxiety, sadness, memory issues, chronic pain, digestive issues, cardiovascular disease, sleep issues, weight problems, and a whole slew of other diseases.

Now think about when you eat a fresh salad with lots of fresh organic veggies. How many megahertz do you think is in that? Again, if you guessed 70-90 MHz, you would be correct! How do you feel after eating a salad? Do you still feel like you have energy? Do you feel vibrant and alive? Lighter and more fluid? Do you feel like you still have energy for the rest of the day? There's a reason behind that! It's all about the amount of energy you are eating and the nutritional value you are getting. It's feeding your body the nutrients it needs. It's energizing you and giving energy to your cells that have been depleted over time due to lack of nutrients, oxygen and hydration. If your thought was, "but I'm still hungry after eating a salad." It could be because your body is actually starving for nutrition. Your cells need the proper nutrients in order to feel good. The SAD food is dead and lifeless. By eating the SAD way, you are actually starving your cells. In America, one of the richest countries in the world, we are one of the most nutrient deficient and starving countries. We're eating a diet void of nutrients, leaving our bodies hungry because we're not receiving the nutrients we need for our bodies to maintain health.

Think about this: Our health not only impacts us, but also our planet. Our planet is emulating the ill health of each of us. Our planet is functioning below the 60-70 MHz. We need to take care of ourselves in order to take care of our world. Another thing to think about... Animal protein and byproducts (milk, butter, eggs, cheese) are completely devoid of energy. How do you feel when you smell a rose? A rose has 320 MHz! Go smell a rose and see what you notice in your body.

Anything you come into contact with has an influence on your body, this includes personal care products with high amounts of chemicals, lawn fertilizers and pesticides, pumping gas, or using your cell phone (or other technology) with the high amounts electromagnetic frequencies (EMF's). This also includes the thoughts you have, the television shows you watch, the air you breathe and the relationships you keep. It all has an impact on your health. These things can bring down your vibrational megahertz. So why not begin to raise it by changing your habits and doing the things within your control?

Eating a diet rich in plant-based, whole-foods nourishes your body and changes the structure and signals you send to it. Your body craves variety and nutrient-dense foods. You begin to crave the foods that are healthy because that is what your body and soul wants and needs. A detox program will help rid you of any cravings you may have for unhealthy foods. And your body will begin to crave kale and sweet potatoes.

I invite you to bring mindfulness to your eating. As you begin to create awareness about eating, it helps to see the way different foods make your body feel.

Create a quiet space, without distractions—TV, computer, books, etc. and focus on your body as you're eating.

Mindful Eating Exercise

Begin by taking a deep breath in through your nose and exhale through your mouth. Feel your body as a whole and feel yourself grounded on the chair your sitting in. Feel yourself being supported by the earth and all that you have. Take another deep breath in through your nose and out through your mouth. Breathe out any tension that you feel in your body. Just allow it to flow through you. With each out breath, feel the tension move out through the pores of your skin.

Tune into your body. What do you notice? Are there any sensations? Do you notice any sensations of hunger? Thirst? What do these feel like? Take a moment and reflect on how that feels in your body. What do you notice? You might ask yourself, "what am I hungry for? What do my cells need"? Just quietly listen to your inner guidance. Trust the answer that emerges.

As you prepare to eat, just take a moment and think about the food you're about to eat. Imagine where it came from before it arrived on your plate. What processes did it go through? Who might have helped in the process? Send them gratitude for what they did to provide you with the meal you're about to eat.

Begin by picking up your food. Can you eat it with your hands? Feel the food between your fingers and ask that the energy of the food matches the energy of your body and provides you with what you need to be nourished. Notice any aromas the food is emitting. How does the smell make your body feel? Notice any sensations. Place the food in your mouth and just embrace all the tastes and textures. What does it feel like in your mouth? Roll it around with your tongue and observe any flavors that arise. Are they salty? Sweet? Savory? Bitter? Pungent? Just notice. Chew your food slowly and observe how your body is beginning to respond to the food. Continue to chew until the food is a watery substance. Swallow slowly and embrace the food. How does the food feel as it is being digested? What physical sensations do you notice? Imagine the food being digested and utilized by all of your cells to nourish your body to the fullest. Continue with this process until you're done eating and feel complete. What signals does your body give you when it is satisfied? How does that feel in your body? Just notice. How does your body feel after eating? What sensations do you notice? Do you feel energized? Tired? Lethargic? Ready to take on the day? Take a deep breath and just notice. Bring this exercise into your day each time your sit down for a meal.

What is Eating Clean?

Eating clean is choosing the cleanest source of foods available that are closest to real food (and the ground) as possible. Nowadays, much of our food supply has been processed and gone through so much handling that by the time you eat it, it is devoid of nutrients. Marketing and packaging may make you think differently, so it's important to stay informed about what you are eating.

What Are Processed Foods, Exactly?

Let's discuss the definition of processed foods. According to foodinsight.org, processed foods are defined as "any deliberate change in a food that occurs before it's available for us to eat. It can be as simple as freezing or drying food to preserve nutrients and freshness, or as complex as formulating a frozen meal with the right balance of nutrients and ingredients". You can find processed foods in a: bag, box, jar, can or any other container you can think of. Basically, if it is not in its whole form, it is processed: A French fry is not a whole food (or a vegetable), but the potato is.

How Did This All Begin?

55

Processing foods began about 2 million years ago with the discovery of fire. Food processing technology has advanced with the innovation of fermentation, canning, jarring, freezing, preserving and dehydrating. We have transferred these technologies to factories and added unnatural chemicals to preserve our food and artificial dyes to color our food. We have moved from natural, whole- foods to the opposite end of the continuum. Many processed foods contain chemicals, dyes, and preservatives that most of us can't pronounce. Eating processed foods have been linked to many diseases including cancer, heart disease, diabetes, autoimmune diseases, depression, and anxiety.

According to a report by Harvard Health Publishing, chronic inflammation is at the root of many of the diseases that we have today, including heart disease, rheumatoid arthritis, cancer, Alzheimer's, and diabetes. Kelly Brogan, MD, reports a strong connection between inflammation and depression and anxiety. Have you ever skinned your knee and then your knee swelled? This is an acute inflammation. It usually gets better within a few days. Chronic inflammation happens in your body when lifestyle choices trigger a response that continually injures your body. These lifestyle factors may include a diet of foods that your body is sensitive to, sugar, processed foods, chemicals, such as pesticides, pathogens, and stress, etc. We are continually putting gas on the fire of inflammation every time we add to the problem. Kelly Brogan explains that once inflammation is active, it is "highly self-perpetuating". The inflammatory cytokines create oxidative stress in our mitochondria. It prevents tryptophan (precursor to serotonin, the feel-good neurotransmitter (more on this in Chapter 5)) from doing its job. It causes other symptoms which induce lethargy, sleep disturbance, social isolation, immobility, low libido, learning disorders, anorexia, and anhedonia.

Start Eating Clean Today by Adding These Soul Loving Practices

Avoid Refined Sugar

I invited Sally to eliminate refined sugar. She heard that sugar is bad and thought she should avoid it, but didn't know where to begin.

A study published by *Scientific Reports* in 2015 found that refined sugar is more addictive than cocaine and 94% of lab mice chose sugar over cocaine. In the Whitehall study, the effects of refined sugar were observed in over 23,000 participants. The study concluded that men consuming more than 67 grams of refined sugar per day were 23% more likely to develop anxiety or depression over the course of five years than those whose sugar consumption was less than 40 grams per day. Their research confirmed "an adverse effect of sugar intake from sweet food/beverage on long-term psychological health and suggests that lower intake of sugar may be associated with better psychological health."

Sugar creates illness and dis-ease in the body including suppressing the immune system, mood shifts in children and adults, depression, anxiety, hyperactivity, feeding cancer cells, causing obesity, and more!

Sugar is in almost everything we eat, from the obvious sweets, to the not so obvious salad dressings, fast food, frozen meals, canned and dried fruit, and wine. These can be sneaky, so read labels. Know your numbers: 4.2 grams of sugar is equal to 1 teaspoon. One cup of cola has 44 grams of sugar which is equal to 10 teaspoons of sugar!

The food industry is very sneaky at putting sugar into our food supply. It's important to know other names for sugar, as it is deviously disguised by the food industry. There are many sugar substitutes which carry their own dangers. These sweeteners are made in a lab and are believed to be linked with diseases such as some cancers, chronic fatigue, Parkinson's disease, Alzheimer's disease, multiple sclerosis, autism, and lupus.

According to sugarscience.com, There Are 61 Names for Sugar and Sugar Substitutes, Including the Following:

- Agave nectar
- Dextrose
- Maple syrup

- Barbados sugar
- Evaporated cane juice
- Molasses
- Barley malt/syrup
- Free-flowing
- brown sugars
- Muscovado
- Beet sugar
- Fructose
- Palm sugar
- Brown sugar
- Fruit juice
- Panocha
- Buttered syrup
- Fruit juice concentrate
- Powdered sugar
- Cane juice/Crystal
- Glucose
- Raw sugar
- Cane sugar
- Glucose solids
- Refiner's syrup
- Caramel
- Golden sugar
- Rice syrup
- Carob syrup
- Golden syrup
- Saccharose
- Castor sugar
- Grape sugar
- Sorghum Syrup
- Coconut palm sugar
- High-Fructose
- Corn Syrup

- Sucrose
- Coconut sugar
- Honey
- Sugar (granulated)
- Confectioner's sugar
- Icing sugar
- Sweet Sorghum
- Corn sweetener
- Invert sugar
- Syrup
- Corn syrup/solids
- Malt syrup
- Treacle
- Date sugar
- Maltodextrin
- Turbinado sugar
- Dehydrated cane juice
- Maltol
- Yellow sugar
- Demerara sugar
- Maltose
- Dextrin
- Mannose

Cook Meals at Home

Sally stopped on her way home from work at the fast food drive through to pick up food for her family's dinner. We talked about incorporating home-cooked meals into her routine. Cooking at home gives you more control over what you're eating because you can read labels, choose what goes into your meal and prepare it with love. Eating at home empowers you to eat less processed foods and refined sugar, know where your meals come from, spend quality time with your family and save on your monthly budget.

Like many adults, Sally was a very busy working mom with little time to cook. We talked about options to help her make healthier choices within her busy schedule. An important part of changing routines is the planning. I encouraged her to plan ahead each week and prepare a menu for a couple nights of the week, since she was new to eating at home. We discussed batch cooking on Sundays, her day off. You can prepare your meals ahead of time. Prepare a big pot of soup for the week; cut up all your veggies to make them easy to grab or for making a salad. If you choose a rice dish, prepare it on Sunday for Tuesday's meal. If you tend to eat lunch on the go, get into the habit of packing your own lunch. Make your lunch the night before or on Sundays for the entire week or eat leftovers. Once you get into the habit, it'll become second nature.

Think Differently About Meat

Sally had always been accustomed to eating meat. She was hesitant to think differently about this. I invite you to look at your meals in a new way. We are accustomed to planning our meals around the meat. I invite you to plan your meals around veggies. Try having smaller portions of meat with your meal and make the rest a colorful rainbow. If you choose to eat meat, choose only the highest quality meats. We live in a time when meat production includes very unethical and improper farming practices. Animals are fed hormones to increase their growth factor and milk production. They are given antibiotics to prevent infections and to kill the bacteria and viruses they encounter while being caged with thousands of other animals. They are fed grain that lacks nutrients and is indigestible, rather than grass. These practices have greatly reduced the quality of meat. Is that the kind of meat you want to put in your body? If you choose to eat meat, choose meats that are grass fed, organic, without hormones or antibiotics. Go one step further and try a meatless day of the week! You might be surprised how satisfied you feel with less meat in your life! Not only will it benefit you, it will also reduce your carbon footprint.

Fill Your Plate With at Least a 50% Rainbow of Vegetables

60

Sally was not used to eating vegetables. Her idea of a veggie was a French fry. So, making this change seemed daunting to her. She began to get excited about it and soon it became something she really enjoyed and actually began to crave! Each meal should consist at least 50% colorful fruits and vegetables. Fruits and vegetables are the closest foods from the earth. Remember the saying, "you are what you eat". When we eat live foods, it gives us energy and vitality. It fuels our cells with the nutrients we need for survival and optimal health. Live foods are rich in water that hydrate the body. When you consume a vast array of colors from fruits and veggies, you are providing your body with all the nutrients each color supplies. Each one has specific vitamins, minerals and antioxidants to give your body what it needs. Have fun with choosing your rainbow and give your veggies a new meaning!

Choose Organic

Sally couldn't understand the hype about organic food. She thought it was a marketing scheme or something that just cost a lot more. We talked about her concerns and the importance of choosing organic whenever possible. Once she understood, she began to consciously make better choices.

What is the hype with organic? What does it all mean? According to the USDA, "Organic food is produced by farmers who emphasize the use of renewable resources and the conservation of soil and water to enhance environmental quality for future generations. Organic meat, poultry, eggs, and dairy products come from animals that are given no antibiotics or growth hormones. Organic food is produced without using most conventional pesticides; fertilizers made with synthetic ingredients or sewage sludge; bioengineering; or ionizing radiation. Before a product can be labeled "organic," a Government-approved certifier inspects the farm where the food is grown to make sure the farmer is following all the rules necessary to meet USDA organic standards. Companies that handle or process organic food before it gets to your local supermarket or restaurant must be certified, too."

Dirty Dozen and the Clean Fifteen

Understanding this concept was refreshing to Sally. She decided to buy what she could within her budget. Why is this important? Choosing to eat organic will help keep the toxins out of the soil, the water, the air and your body. According to Beyondpesticides.org, traditional farming practices that are not organic have heavy build ups of toxic chemicals that have been known to cause disease, including cancer, autism, asthma, and more. You might be thinking that organic is more expensive, but in the long term it is less expensive than large medical bills. Sally learned about the options for buying produce even if it isn't organic by referring to the Clean 15 and Dirty Dozen models. The Dirty Dozen is a list of fruits and vegetables that should be purchased organic because they have the highest amount of pesticides when conventionally grown. The Clean Fifteen is a list of fruits and vegetables that have the least amount of pesticides when conventionally grown. It is ok to purchase non-organic fruits and vegetables on this list. The Environmental Working Group updates this list annually. Visit ewg.org for more information.

Choose Plant-foods, Choose Whole-foods

As Sally and I continued our work together, she was experiencing positive effects from the dietary changes she was making. She was starting to feel really vibrant, energized and the fog was beginning to lift. Making these changes in her diet increased her awareness of her connection to her mind and soul. Sally was interested in taking her lifestyle to a whole new level. She knew I was a strong advocate for a plant-based diet and wanted to learn more. Sally and I began to discuss the value of this lifestyle.

Plant-based, whole-foods = real foods primarily from plant sources. Whole-foods are those foods that are in their natural state, as close to coming out of the ground as possible. When we choose whole-foods, we are getting the nutrients our body needs in order to be healthy. A whole- food diet includes choosing foods in their natural state to increase your nutrient-density and avoiding nutrient-poor processed foods. Whole-foods mainly include plant-based foods such as vegetables, fruits, nuts, seeds, legumes and whole grains. A whole-foods diet provides you with all of the nutrients you need for optimal health.

The Evidence for a Plant-based, Whole-foods Lifestyle is Undeniable

The benefits of a plant-based, whole-foods lifestyle are undeniable. It is overwhelmingly clear that choosing to eat more plants in your diet has an abundance of benefits that not only will help you live longer, but also help you heal from dis-ease. When we realize that our food choices are within our control and we are no longer influenced by propaganda and marketing messages, we begin to wake up and make the connection between what we eat and how we feel. We begin to be conscious of the important choices we make every day. Read on to learn the many reasons for eating clean and adopting a plant-based, whole-foods lifestyle.

Eating a Plant-based, Whole-foods Diet Helps Prevent and Reverse Lifestyle-induced Diseases (Including Depression and Anxiety!)

Sally was overweight and had overactive thyroid when she arrived in my office. She had no idea that her health was linked to the food she ate. We talked about how our bodies will naturally heal themselves when given the proper nutrients. Our cells are continually regenerating, cleaning and healing themselves. Changing your diet to a plant-based lifestyle has been shown to speed the healing process. Forget about what you were taught about disease being "irreversible!" According to Michael Greger, MD, in his book *How Not to Die*, he inarguably validates the research and demonstrates that eating plants has been shown to reverse diseases such as heart disease, lung disease, cancers, diabetes, high blood pressure, kidney disease, suicidal depression, and even Parkinson's disease!

You'll Get a Rainbow of Variety

Sally couldn't believe how much variety she could have! She began experimenting with the different foods and making new dishes she had never tried before. Have you ever wandered around the produce section or scoped out the bins of grains, nuts, seeds, beans and legumes. So many varieties! I encourage you to take some time and look at the assortment of options available. There are multitudes of plants and an array of colors, tastes and textures to choose from; you could have a different meal every day for months. It's important to incorporate as much of the rainbow as possible, because each color represents a different nutrient composition.

- Red vegetables such as tomatoes have lycopene, which is a powerful antioxidant that eliminates free radicals (toxins), prevents cancer, contributes to eye health, heart health and bone health.

- Orange vegetables such as carrots have an abundance of carotenoids, including beta carotene which supports healthy skin, reduces chronic inflammation, builds a strong immune system, and contributes to eye health and brain health

- Yellow vegetables such as yellow bell peppers have zeaxanthin and lutein which supports skin health, including premature aging, reduces chronic inflammation, protects the skin from ultraviolet rays, supports heart health, and protects against free radicals.

- Green vegetables, such as your leafy greens and Brussel sprouts, have chlorophyll, as well as an abundance of other nutrients that support building blood, detoxification, prevent cancer, support skin health, fights free radicals, reduce chronic inflammation and rejuvenate cellular health.

- Purple vegetables, such as purple cabbage, contain resveratrol and anthocyanin which help to reduce inflammation, support heart health, reduce chronic inflammation, prevent cancer, and prevent decline in the aging brain.

- White vegetables, such as onions, are comprised of allicin; cauliflower has sulforaphane. These play a role is preventing cancer, building immunity, reducing chronic inflammation, and supporting heart health, and brain health.

Every color group has something amazing to offer. Not only do they provide essential nutrients, each one contains much more than listed here. It's easy to get into the mindset of taking supplements for the nutrients you need. You can find a supplement for every nutrient listed here. However, we can't take a pill to get rid of our ailments. It's important to eat a whole-foods diet to fully absorb the nutrients we need. When we isolate nutrients and put them into capsule form, we are not getting the complete nutrients found in the fruit or vegetable.

No More Counting Calories

Sally couldn't believe that she could eat food and not worry about calories! She could eat healthy foods and enjoy every bite. Have you been conditioned to count calories? That is the old way of thinking! When you eat a plant-based, whole-foods diet that includes a rainbow of variety, your diet includes almost all of the nutrients your body needs. The only exception is vitamin B12. In addition, if you do not get enough sunshine, you may need vitamin D. By eating a balanced array of plant-based, whole-foods you will never have to count calories again. How freeing is that?

A Note About Vitamin B12 and Vitamin D

Vitamin B12

B12 is a vital nutrient that cannot be obtained sufficiently from today's plant sources. Vitamin B12 is produced by bacteria found in dirt and because our soils have been depleted due to pesticides and chemical fertilizers, it lacks the proper amounts we need. Furthermore, through the washing process to eliminate pathogens, we wipe our fruits and vegetables clean which contributes to this nutrient being further depleted. Animals do not naturally contain B12 either, but because they

eat plants grown in the dirt or the flesh of other animals, they produce their own B12 from the
bacteria in their gut. B12 is a water-soluble vitamin so it is not stored in your body and needs to be ingested on a regular basis. It is recommended that you take at least 10 mcg per day in supplement form or eat foods that are fortified or contain B12 two times per day.

Ways to get Vitamin B12

- Eat more fermented foods such as sauerkraut, rejuvelac, and tempeh.
- Nutritional yeast fortified with B12.
- Almond milk fortified with B12.
- Edible, dried green and purple seaweed including nori.
- Find a good quality sublingual supplement. Choose vitamin B12 in the methylcobalamin form which is the methylated form of B12 and is more bioavailable and ready for our bodies to use.

Vitamin D

Vitamin D plays many roles in health including bone strength, improving mood, thyroid regulation, calcium absorption, and muscle function. Vitamin D is more like a hormone that our bodies make, than a vitamin. However, depending on the season and the latitude of where you live, we often do not make enough and need to get it from other sources. Many people are deficient in Vitamin D, regardless of the food they eat, especially those living in climates that are cold and dark in the winter months, have indoor jobs, or have very dark skin. If you are concerned about your Vitamin D levels, have your Vitamin D levels checked by your physician. It's important to find ways to get more Vitamin D in your life to promote overall wellness. The current recommendation for vitamin D is 400 IU per day for children and 600 IU adults up to 50 years old, and 700 IU for adults over 70 years old. However, talk with your healthcare practitioner about the amount your body needs.

Ways to get Vitamin D

- Expose yourself to at least 30 minutes of sunlight per day during the peak times or until your skin turns a light pink.
- Eat mushrooms.
- Fortified foods such as tofu or plant milks (hemp, almond, soy, etc.)
- A good quality liposomal Vitamin D supplement

You'll Lose Weight Naturally!

Sally, once overweight, began losing weight naturally. She didn't just lose the weight but kept it off because she was not in the yo-yo diet cycle. She changed her eating habits and found out doing this was so effective!

As you begin to choose foods that are whole, and plant-based, you'll notice that weight begins to drop! Because you're no longer eating non-nutritious, processed junk, and you are feeding your body the nutrient-rich foods it really craves, your body begins to detoxify naturally. Fat cells begin to decrease because you're finally giving your body what it needs. Nutrition!

Cravings Begin to Disappear or Change!

Sally had major cravings for salty foods. Chips and pizza were her foods of choice. She started to notice that as she began to shift her focus toward healthy foods, her cravings began to change. She started to crave kale and Brussel sprouts!

Do you currently experience cravings? Eating a diet rich in plant-based, whole-foods nourishes your body and changes the structure and signals you send to it. Your body craves variety and nutrient-dense foods. You begin to crave the foods that are healthy because that is what your body wants and needs. Going through a detox program will help rid you of any cravings you may have for unhealthy foods. Your body will begin to crave kale and sweet potatoes! Crazy, I know! But it happens.

So, let's look at the different cravings. There's usually a deeper reason behind them.

Do you crave salts? This is probably an indication of a mineral deficiency. How do you add more salt to your diet? Try leafy greens, vegetables, Celtic Sea Salt, legumes, nuts, seeds, fruits, whole grains, and sea vegetables.

Do you crave sugar? Too much sugar in your body can produce more sugar. So, eating a bowl of pasta will essentially convert into sugar, setting you up for more cravings later. Too much sugar can also create a yeast build up in your system and when you continue to feed the yeast, the more cravings for sugar you will have. So, what to do? Try adding in sweet vegetables when you have a craving, beneficial bacterial such as cultured vegetables, eliminate sweets, or try stevia, a natural sweetener.

Do you experience emotional cravings? Experiencing anxiety, depression or emotional voids can create cravings for emotional reasons. We tend to fill that void with food. Next time you are beginning to grab something that is processed or unhealthy, ask yourself "What am I really hungry for?" You might be surprised to discover that you need a hug, someone to talk to, or to follow your passions.

You'll Get All the Protein You Need

Sally, like many people, grew up believing that she could only get protein from animal sources. She had no idea the amount of protein contained in plants. She was amazed to learn that she could get all of her nutritional needs met, including protein, through eating plants.

There are lots of myths about not getting enough protein from plants. Our culture is taught that more protein is better, and we can only get it from animal sources. This is a false claim. Our body takes in what it needs and either excretes the rest or stores it as fat. This is true of too much protein. According to the Plantrician Project, studies have shown that the average plant-based, whole-foods diet meets or exceeds the recommended daily protein intake set by most official nutrition organizations. The recommended amount for a 160-pound adult is 58 grams of protein per day (0.8 grams per kilogram of bodyweight). The Plantrician Project includes a sample meal plan for a day which clearly demonstrates how eating a plant-based, whole-foods diet will give you an adequate amount of protein.

Sample Meal	Grams of Protein
Breakfast: 1 cup of oatmeal with blueberries, walnuts and 1 cup of organic nut milk	17 grams
Lunch: Split pea soup, whole grain bread with hummus, and a garden salad	21 grams
Snack: Apple and peanut butter	4 grams
Dinner: Mexican black beans and brown rice in corn tortillas with avocado and salsa	18 grams
Total:	60 grams

What's Good for the Body and Mind, Is Also Good for the Environment

Sally became more conscious of her surroundings and the ways her choices impacted the rest of the world. She was thrilled to learn that by choosing a plant-based lifestyle she could make a difference reducing her carbon footprint. It takes a lot of resources and energy to produce meat. According to the Plantrician Project, it takes 12,000 gallons of water to produce just 10 pounds of beef. That's enough water for a family of 4 for an entire year! According to the Water Footprint Network, it takes 1,000 gallons of water to produce just ONE gallon of milk. According to onegreenplanet.org, the United Nations Food and Agriculture Organization (FAO) livestock production is responsible for 14.5 percent of global greenhouse gas emissions, while other organizations like the Worldwatch Institute have estimated it could be as much as 51 percent. Three-hundred million tons of manure produced by factory farms are responsible for 37 percent of agricultural greenhouse gas emissions. Manure and its factory farming practices produce massive quantities of methane, a gas that warms the earth 20 times faster than carbon dioxide.

If you're new to eating healthy, please be kind to yourself. Make one change at a time. Doing this has been shown to be the most sustainable approach. Add in one new thing per week and build from there. I invite you to view these changes as a lifestyle rather than a diet. Diets don't work and are usually a temporary fix. It is important to get to the root cause of your physical and emotional dis-ease. Making these changes will help move you in that direction. Your body, mind and soul will thank you for it. Thank yourself for giving yourself the gift of healthy foods.

CHAPTER FIVE

Your Gut is Your Second Brain

"If there's one thing to know about the human body; it's this: the human body has a ringmaster. This ringmaster controls your digestion, your immunity, your brain, your weight, your health and even your happiness. This ringmaster is the gut"
~ *Nancy Mure*

Gut health has been on the radar for many health professionals and researchers for a long time and there is a good reason why. Research is showing how important gut health to our wellbeing. You may have heard of the term "leaky gut" which is another word for intestinal permeability. According to a published article in *Frontiers in Immunology*, "the intestinal epithelial lining, together with factors secreted from it, forms a barrier that separates the host from the environment. In pathologic conditions, the permeability of the epithelial lining may be compromised allowing the passage of toxins, antigens, and bacteria in the lumen to enter the blood stream creating a "leaky gut". This has many implications for people today.

There are many factors that contribute to gut health including processed foods, toxic environment, overprescribed antibiotics, unknown food sensitivities, pesticides, herbicides, genetically modified organisms (GMO's), etc. All of these factors play a role in destroying the lining of the gut and the microbiome. The microbiome makes up all of the bacteria in the gut, the good and the bad. We need the good bacteria in order to take out the bad and create a healthy immune system and functioning gut. Disease and health begins in the gut. According to Norman Walker, who writes in his book *Colon Health*, constipation is the body's greatest enemy. Many people are constipated and it is a symptom of a much larger issue. When nutrients cannot be absorbed through the colon, they begin to putrefy, ferment and pollute the blood stream with pathogens and dis-ease producing bacteria. Constipation also interferes with the assimilation of vital intestinal flora. According to the Gut Health Project, we could be carrying between 5-20 pounds of fecal matter that is toxifying our bodies. There are over 170 diseases linked to constipation and gut health. Constipation is not a normal occurrence, in fact, it has many health repercussions.

Ways to Heal a Leaky Gut

1. Try the 2-week elimination diet (Chapter 6)
2. Stress management techniques like breathing and meditation (Chapters 2 and 3)
3. Eat a clean plant-based, organic diet of whole-foods (Chapter 4)
4. Incorporate foods rich in probiotics (at the end of this chapter)
5. Consider taking L-Glutamine to support your gut lining which has been known to help support and repair leaky gut. You take this as a supplement or find it naturally in asparagus and broccoli.

6. Remove any over the counter medications. Take antibiotics only when absolutely necessary. Eliminate alcohol and other drugs.

What's Good for the Body is Good for the mind

As Sally began to change her diet, we were able to focus on the integrity of her gut health. She reported feeling bloated, acid reflux, and moodiness throughout the day, especially after eating. Eating a diet full of processed foods, meat and dairy can create deficiencies in amino acids, minerals and mineral cofactors which contribute to the production of important neurotransmitters. New areas of research are concluding that the gut is considered the 2nd brain. It has its own neural network and production of neurotransmitters which play a major role in how we feel. According to *Scientific American*, we have around 100 million neurons firing in the gut. Studies show strong evidence pointing to gut health strongly impacting mood. Eating processed foods, taking antibiotics, and chronic stress can all play a role in damaging the lining of the gut and creating an imbalance of gut flora and neurotransmitters.

Neurotransmitters play a crucial role in how we feel, and may cause depression, anxiety and insomnia if not supported properly. In fact, 95% of the neurotransmitter serotonin (responsible for processing emotions and improving mood) is found in the gut. Neurotransmitters transmit impulses throughout the central nervous system and impact mental health and physiological functions. Amino acids are needed for the production of neurotransmitters. And where can you get these amino acids? Plants! According to Dr. Eric Braverman, author of *The Edge Effect*, you can boost your diet with these important neurotransmitters.

Neurotransmitters

GABA

73

Low GABA levels are linked to anxiety, panic attacks, agitation, stress and poor sleep. When your levels are sufficient you are calm and stress free. Increase your GABA by incorporating these high glutamic acid foods, which helps to produce GABA:

Glutamic Acid/Glutamate (forms glutamine) mgs 6-8 oz per serving

Broccoli	740 mg
Brown rice	940 mg
Spinach	680 mg
Banana	220 mg
Oranges	210 mg
Almonds	10.3 g
Oats	7.4 g
Potato	830 mg
Lentils	2.8 g
Walnuts	5.4 g
Rice bran	3.7 g

Serotonin

Low levels of serotonin are linked to depression, sleep problems, anger, PMS, cravings, and addictive behaviors. When your levels are sufficient you feel calm, relaxed, and confident. Increase your serotonin levels by increasing tryptophan or 5-HTP with these foods:

Food	Amount	Content (G)
Avocado	1	0.40
Chocolate	1 cup	0.11
Granola	1 cup	0.20
Oat flakes	1 cup	0.20
Butternut squash seeds	½ cup	0.20
Spirulina	¾ cup	0.74
Soybeans	¼ cup	0.478

Other ways to increase serotonin levels include moderate and regular exercise and natural sunlight.

Dopamine

Low levels of dopamine are linked to depression, excessive sleep, digestive problems, cravings, anger, guilt, mood swings, procrastination and self-destructive thoughts. When your levels are sufficient you feel energized, focused and alert. Increase your dopamine levels by increasing the following foods with high levels of tyrosine, which helps to produce dopamine and stress hormones such as norepinephrine (noradrenaline) and epinephrine (adrenaline) which supports catecholamine production.

Common Signs That Your Gut Flora May Need a Tune-up

Food	Amount	Content (G)
Chocolate	6-8 oz.	0.40
Granola	1 cup	0.40
Rolled Oats or oat	1 cup	0.35
Kidney beans	1/3 cup	1.01

These foods, high in phenylalanine, convert to tyrosine and synthesizes into dopamine and may decrease depression and fatigue.

Food	Amount	Content (G)
Dark Chocolate	2-4 oz.	0.40
Granola	1 cup	0.65
Rolled Oats or oat	1 cup	0.50
Soybeans	6-8 oz.	1.20
Walnuts	6-8 oz.	1.40

Supporting Your Gut

If you read about health, you've probably heard about probiotics. But what have you heard about *pre*biotics? What is a prebiotic? Prebiotics are the ingredients in the foods we eat that support the growth of the good bacteria in our gut. Prebiotics are found in the insoluble fiber of plants we eat; the most common ones are inulin and oligosaccharides. It has been shown that these food molecules play a major role in your health, together with the good bacteria including bifidobacteria and lactobacilli, reduce disease producing bacteria such as clostridia, klebsiella, and Enterobacter (Lipski, 2005). Prebiotics help to increase absorption of minerals, such as calcium, magnesium, zinc and iron in the digestive track. Where do you get prebiotics, you might ask? Plants!!

Eat the Following Prebiotics to Support Your Gut

- Jerusalem artichokes
- Onions
- Chicory
- Garlic
- Leeks
- Organic soybeans
- Peas
- Legumes
- Eggplant
- Burdock root
- Asparagus
- Sugar maple
- Chinese chive
- Whole rye
- Whole wheat
- Fruit, such as bananas

According to Elizabeth Lipski, in her book *Digestive Wellness*, eating just 2.75 grams per day will begin to increase your good bacteria and eliminate the bad!

Why Eat Probiotic Foods?

Probiotics are the good bacteria and important to include in your diet as they assist in building immunity, lining your gut and helping with nutrient absorption. There are many factors that can lead to gut imbalances which include processed foods and eating foods that contain antibiotics such as factory farmed meat and dairy, over-prescribed antibiotics that kill off not only the bad bacteria, but the good bacteria, leaving your body susceptible to immunity problems.

Common Signs That Your Gut Flora May Need a Tune-up

76

- Constipation
- Gas and bloating
- Chronic diarrhea
- PMS
- Hormonal issues
- Candida
- Vitamin B deficiencies
- High cholesterol
- Dairy allergies
- Osteoporosis
- Severe bruising
- Vaginal infections
- Neurological problems
- Autoimmune conditions
- Skin issues
- Frequent colds and flu

Benefits of Adding Probiotic-rich Foods to Your Diet

- Stronger immune system
- Improved digestion
- Improved moods
- Increased energy from production of vitamin B12
- Healthier skin, including improvement in eczema and psoriasis
- Decreased colds and flus
- Better breath because probiotics destroy candida and reduce halitosis
- Healing from leaky gut and inflammatory bowel disease
- Weight loss

Probiotic-rich Foods

Kefir

Kefir is a fermented drink that can be made from milk, water, coconut milk and coconut water. Kefir is made from kefir bacteria grains which ferment in a mixture of water or milk and sugar. Kefir has about 30-56 strains of good bacteria and when drank the body utilizes it more effectively than yogurt, because the curd size is much smaller, has more absorbable beneficial bacteria and colonizes the digestive track. Health benefits include: eliminates constipation, supports the digestive process, reduces allergies, heals yeast infections, promotes sleep, assists in helping the body restore balance after antibiotic use. You can make this yourself or buy it in the store. Pay attention to the sugar content when purchasing kefir. Make sure it has a low sugar content to reap the benefits.

Kombucha

Kombucha is a living health drink that is made by fermenting tea and sugar with a SCOBY culture, which is a mixture of yeast and bacteria. As it ferments, the sugar is consumed by the culture and provides a very tangy and tart probiotic drink. Kombucha has been known for its health benefits which include assisting in the detoxification process. It contains lots of B vitamins and amino acids, improves digestion, boosts the immune system, relieves headaches, migraines and joint pain. You can make this yourself or buy it in the store. Pay attention to the sugar content when purchasing kombucha. Make sure it has a low sugar content to reap the benefits.

Apple Cider Vinegar

Fermented apple cider vinegar is made from fresh crushed apples and allowed to mature in tanks, which boosts its natural fermented qualities. When mature, it contains a web-like substance, called "the mother", that becomes visible when the rich brownish liquid is held to the light. Don't be confused by the refined and distilled vinegars which do not provide the same benefits. Health benefits of apple cider vinegar include: kills bacteria, lowers blood sugar, promotes digestive process, may lower cholesterol and risk of heart disease, may inhibit cancer growth, assists with detoxification and may reduce acid reflux. You can make this yourself or buy it in the store. I recommend buying organic and make sure the label says it contains "the mother."

Rejuvelac

Rejuvelac is a fermented beverage that is inexpensive and easy to make. It is made by fermenting sprouted grains such as kamut, wheat berries, quinoa, etc. in water for 3-7 days. Health benefits include: loaded with vitamins B (including B12), K and E, proteins; and enzymes. It is beneficial to your digestive system, promotes a healthy intestinal environment, improves skin health, has anti-inflammatory properties. I have not seen this in the stores. Making it yourself is easy. There are many recipes online to choose from.

Sauerkraut

Sauerkraut is made from cabbage and salt, mixed together and set aside to ferment for several weeks. Don't be confused by sauerkraut that is cultured, pickled and preserved that you'll usually find in the condiment aisle. This is not the same as fermented sauerkraut and does not offer the same health benefits. Health benefits of sauerkraut include: Aids in digestion, builds immunity, assists with eliminating candida, reduces allergies, has anti-inflammatory properties. You can make this yourself or buy it in the store. You will find it in the refrigerated section. Make sure it is not pasteurized.

Miso

Miso is a paste typically made from soybeans or other beans such as garbanzo beans, sea salt and koji, which is a mold starter. It can be mixed with rice, barley or other grains. The mixture is fermented anywhere from 3 months to 3 years. Health benefits of miso include: It contains all essential amino acids making it a complete protein; assists in digestive process; replaces good gut flora; may inhibit cancer growth; strengthens and enhances the immune system; and protects against free radicals. I recommend purchasing organic or making it from organic beans.

Tempeh

There's a lot of controversy around soy products in the health world, but when it comes to soy, tempeh stands apart due to being the least processed form of soy and its fermentation qualities. Tempeh is closer to a whole-food than any other form of processed soy, and the fermentation process increases its digestibility, soy proteins, nutrients, and can increase the amount of vitamin K when paired with Bacillus subtilis in the fermentation process. Health benefits of tempeh: Boosts immunity, increases bone density, reduces cholesterol, and increases gut flora. I recommend purchasing organic or making it from organic soybeans.

I invite you to thank yourself for creating the space and investing the time toward making lifestyle changes for yourself. Remember, it doesn't have to happen overnight. Take what feels good to you and incorporate that into your life. Try one thing at a time. Healing the gut takes time. Be patient and loving toward yourself as you move through your healing journey.

CHAPTER SIX

Detox Your Body, Detox Your Mind

*When you take the time to cleanse your physical body of accumulated stress and toxicity, you are
rewarded with increased vitality and optimal health.* ~Debbie Ford

Your Body Is the Temple for Your Soul

Detoxification plays a big part in getting well, moving toward
feeling good and releasing anxiety and depression. Remember, these are
symptoms of something bigger. When you detoxify your body, you're
detoxifying all the heavy stuff that is weighing you down (literally and
figuratively). If you think about all the toxins you ingest on a daily basis
from food, air, water and beyond, just think about how many toxins are
stored in your body over a lifetime! These toxins build up and wreak
havoc on your systems and as a result those systems begin
malfunctioning. Think about a car. If you never took the car in for an oil
change, what would happen? The oil becomes dirty over time, dries up
and the engine seizes. The body works the same way. It needs regular

maintenance and care. It requires care to eliminate the things that no longer serve your health and wellbeing.

Your body is the temple for your soul. It's the only body you get in this lifetime, and your soul wants you to take care of it. A buildup of toxins, whether it's heavy metals, parasites, chemicals or other substances creates an overload which then creates dis-ease in the body. The result is depression or anxiety. Your body is meant to heal naturally and when you stop feeding it toxic fuel and start providing it with the nutrients it needs, it begins to relax and let go of the waste and make room for healing.

I suggested that Sally begin a detoxification program to help release the toxins that had been building up over her lifetime and creating havoc in her body and affecting how she felt. Taking care of your body and starting by detoxifying the different organs of your body can be one of the kindest things you do to support repairing your body so it functions efficiently again.

What Is Detoxification?

So, what exactly is detoxification? It is the process of removing toxins or toxic buildup from the body. Our bodies benefit from detoxification when we become overloaded with heavy metals, free radicals, unbalanced gut bacteria, parasites, or candida overgrowth. Toxicity can interfere with the functioning of your body, including physical and mental wellbeing. It is important to take a proactive approach to cleansing the body from these toxins.

How Do We Become Toxic?

Toxicity can build up from the foods we eat, including pesticide and herbicide residue on food, processed foods, sugar, water we drink, the environment we live and the air we breathe, chemicals we use in our homes, drugs and alcohol, stress and negative emotions, and unhealthy relationships. Since you're living on the planet, most likely eating a SAD, working and living a fast-paced life, breathing the air, and drinking tap water, you could benefit from a detoxification plan.

How Do You Know If You're Toxic?

Sally was experiencing chronic fatigue, low energy, foggy mind, and achy joints, all of which she contributed to aging! Many people are walking around with symptoms that "seem normal," and have adjusted to their symptoms because they believe that is a part of aging. The truth is, we are not meant to feel exhausted all the time or get sick as we age. Toxins in the environment, in addition to unprocessed emotions and negative thoughts, build up to toxic levels in our bodies and create illness. We must become conscious of this. In fact, a new field of study called epi-genetics concludes that our genes that carry the code for certain diseases get turned on through lifestyle choices, **not** a genetic destiny for that disease. In other words, we're not destined to get cancer just because "it runs in our family." We might have a predisposition for it, but we have a say. We control our genetic destiny through our choices of what we eat, the water we drink, the air we breathe, etc. This is why detoxification is so important. Learning and implementing the strategies in this book will help you to live the life you are meant to live and release the genes-are-my-destiny fear. You can do something about it and empower yourself, empower your soul!

Here's an Exercise to Illustrate the Point

- Get a pen. Now hold the pen tightly in your hand.
- The pen represents your toxins, and the hand is your awareness.
- Notice that although gripping the pen is uncomfortable, after a little time it begins to feel familiar or "normal." Are you feeling that yet?
- In this same way, your awareness holds on tightly to the toxins, feeling tired with low energy and eventually you get used to holding on and you don't even realize you're doing it. It just becomes a part of you.

- Now open your hand and roll the pen around on your palm. Notice that the pen and your hand are not attached to each other.
- The same is true for the toxins that are weighing you down. The toxins and illness are no more attached to you than the pen is attached to your hand.
- Now turn your hand over and let the pen go.
- What happened? The pen dropped to the floor.
- Was it hard? No, you simply stopped holding on and let go.
- That is what it means to take control of your health. You make a choice to let go of the toxins and realize that your health is in YOUR hands.

You May Need to Begin a Detoxification Program If You Experience

Any of the Following Signs:

- Headaches
- Foggy mind
- Joint pain
- Skin rashes
- Depression
- Anxiety
- Mood swings
- Fatigue
- Sinus congestion
- Excess mucous
- Allergies
- Frequent colds
- Autoimmunity
- Sore throat
- Backaches
- Constipation
- Chemical sensitivity
- Acne
- Sleep problems

What Are the Benefits of Detoxification?

- Prevent and reverse illness
- Decrease in anxiety and depression
- Weight loss
- Give digestion a rest
- Improve sleep
- Clear skin
- Emotional balance
- Improve mental clarity
- Increased energy
- Slows the aging process
- Restore balance in the body

84

What to Expect During Detoxification

- Dizziness
- Mood swings
- Irritability
- Lethargy
- Headaches
- Cravings

- Acne
- Digestive Problems
- Exhaustion
- Sleep disturbances
- Cold or Flu like Symptoms

These symptoms are all a natural part of the detoxification process. As your body releases toxins, your body may go through a "healing crisis" or Jarisch-Herxheimer reaction. This is when your body feels worse before it feels better, i.e., you experience detoxification symptoms. These symptoms are temporary. As you're going through the healing response, your body is releasing toxins. Drinking lots of water, sweating and using the tips listed below will help rid your body of the toxins faster. The body releases toxins from different channels in the body including the respiratory, digestive and urinary tracts, and through the skin. It's important to incorporate different cleansing tools for each system. The symptoms can also be lessened by doing a colon cleanse before other organ detoxifications. It's important to start with a colon cleanse to allow the body space to release all other toxins. If the colon is not clear, other toxins may go into the bloodstream when you are detoxifying and the detoxification process will be a lot tougher for the system to handle and could take longer. Please talk to your health care professional before taking on a cleansing or detoxification program.

Types of Detoxification and Cleanses
The Elimination Diet

Food allergies and sensitivities can be triggers for anxiety and depression. When foods are not agreeing with you (even so called healthy foods), your body may feel depressed or anxious, among other things. Learning to listen to your body will help you learn to reconnect with it and understand what it needs. Your body talks to you in subtle ways at first. It will whisper to you and it is up to you to learn to hear those whispers. The whispers turn into screams when ignored. You can learn to tune into the frequency at which your body talks to you and reverse and heal dis-ease. As I mentioned in previous chapters, what goes into your body is a big deal when it comes to feeling good. Allergies develop over time. It really doesn't matter if you've eaten the same thing for years, your body can grow to not like something. While an allergy test may produce some answers for true allergies, it will not give you accurate results for foods sensitivities. Many food sensitivities may cause the symptoms of depression and anxiety, along with other physical symptoms, such as fatigue and foggy mind. The only way to know if a particular food is the culprit is to remove it from your system. From the time a food is ingested, it can take up to 3 days or more for a symptom to appear! This is why the connection between foods and symptoms is not always seen right away.

You can determine food allergies and sensitivities by eliminating the most common food allergens such as:

- Gluten
- Corn
- Shellfish
- Nightshades
- Soy
- Citrus
- Most animal protein
- Nuts
- Caffeine
- Alcohol
- Processed foods
- Dairy

Try eliminating these foods from your diet for 2 to 3 weeks and then reintroduce 1 food every 3 days to see how your body responds. Going through this process will help you understand what your body needs, what makes you feel good and what creates the symptoms. Remember, just because it's a "health" food doesn't mean your body likes it.

So, you might ask, what *can* I eat? Well, you are in luck! We are fortunate to have such a variety of foods to eat that don't create symptoms. If you're not used to these foods, remember, there is a learning curve to changing any health habit. Please take time to be gentle with yourself and remember that it's a process.

Here's a List of Delicious and Yummy Foods You Can Eat!

Whole Grains:
Amaranth
Brown Rice
Quinoa
White Jasmine Rice
Wild Rice

Legumes:
Adzuki Beans
Black Beans
Garbanzo Beans
Lima Beans
Mung Beans
White Beans

Flour:
Brown rice flour
Quinoa flour
Garbanzo bean
Flour
Coconut flour

Fruits:
Apples
Apricots (fresh or dried
with no added preservatives)
Bananas
Blackberries
Blueberries

Vegetables:
Artichoke
Asparagus
Avocados
Beets
Bok Choy
Broccoli
Brussels Sprouts
Cabbage
Carrots
Cauliflower
Celeriac
Celery
Chard
Cilantro
Coriander
Collard Greens
Cucumber
Fennel
Garlic
Ginger root
Jerusalem Artichoke
Kale
Lettuce
Mushrooms
Mustard Greens
Onions
Parsley
Parsnip
Peas (sugar snap, snow,

Oils:
Extra Virgin Olive Oil
Virgin Coconut Oil

Sweeteners:
Coconut Sugar
Coconut Nectar
Pure Maple Syrup
Raw Honey

Herbal Teas:
Astragalus
Burdock
Chamomile
Dandelion Root
Licorice
Mint
Nettle
Rooibos
Rose
Slippery Elm
Tulsi (holy basil)

Herbs & Spices:
Allspice
Anise
Bay leaves
Black pepper
Cumin
Coriander
Cinnamon

Cherries
Dates (dried or fresh with no preservatives or additives) Figs (fresh and dried) Grapes
Melons
Nectarines ` Peaches
Pears
Pineapple
Plantains
Papayas
Plums
Pomegranates
Raspberries

Sea Vegetables:
Nori
Kombu
Hijiki
Arame
Dulse

frozen, and dried split)
Pickles (homemade without chilies)
Pumpkin
Rutabaga
Spinach
Sweet Potatoes
String Beans
Turnips
Winter Squash
Watercress
Yams
Zucchini

Seeds & Butters:
Raw Pine Nuts
Raw Hemp Seeds
Raw Chia
Raw Flax Seeds
Raw Pumpkin Seeds
Raw Sunflower Seeds
Pumpkin Seed Butter

Turmeric
Ginger (Fresh and powder)
Nutmeg
Cloves
Oregano
Thyme
Basil Dill
Raw Organic Vanilla Powder

Other
Raw Apple Cider Vinegar
Raw Coconut Vinegar
Coconut Aminos
Fresh Coconut Water
Coconut Milk (canned, organic)
Fresh Coconut Meat
Raw Coconut Butter

Lymph System

The lymphatic system is a one-way drainage system that transports white blood cells that fight infection called lymph fluid from the body tissues into the blood circulation. It helps the body get rid of toxins and waste. According to Livescience.com, there are 600 to 700 lymph nodes in the body, the spleen being the largest lymphatic organ. If you don't maintain your lymph system, it can become overloaded with toxins. The tonsils are also a part of the lymphatic system and are responsible for creating antibodies and lymphocytes and serve as filters.

The thymus gland is a part of the lymphatic system and the endocrine system which is located in the middle of the chest above the heart. This organ is typically biggest at birth and begins to shrink thereafter turning into fatty tissue as we age and then becomes dormant. It assists in producing antibodies and in controlling the immune system. The lymph system does not have a pump for circulating and moving waste matter through, so it needs some assistance from us to move the lymph and clean it out. Here are a few ways to move your lymph:

Cleansing the Lymph

Deep Breathing

Deep breathing is one of the best ways to help stimulate the flow of lymph, release the toxins through the respiratory tract, as well as assist in relieving anxiety and depression. Three times a day set a timer and take 10 deep breaths in through your nose and out through your mouth, inhale for a count of 4, hold for 8, exhale for 4 counts.

Rebounding

Jumping on a small trampoline or rebounder for 10 to 15 minutes per day can stimulate the flow of lymph. If you can't get a rebounder, try jumping jacks!

Drink Plenty of Water

Water will help move any stagnant waste. Humans are 75 to 85% water so it's vital that are bodies are replenished to run efficiently. Drink at least ½ your body weight in ounces per day. Drink more if you are active. ex: if you weigh 140 lbs., drink 70 oz. per day. Drink from a clean filtered source, if possible.

Dry Brushing

Buy a brush with dry bristles. Dry brushing your skin will increase the flow of lymph. Brush in circular strokes starting at your feet, working all your body parts and brush toward your heart.

Thump the Thymus

The lymphatic system is the name for the various lymph tissues and cells in the body. The central lymph tissues include the thymus gland, the bone marrow, the lymph nodes, the spleen and tonsils, and sections found behind the epithelial layer of the gastrointestinal mucosa called gut associated lymphoid tissue. Over time, the thymus shrinks and stops functioning effectively. By thumping the thymus regularly, you can begin to reactivate it. Also, it has been known to grow in size by doing this.

Cleansing the Colon

According to Norman Walker, who wrote the book *Colon Health*, health begins in the colon and by eating a diet full of fried and processed foods, excess sugar and salt, our colons become a breeding ground for disease. It is important to care for your colon health and understand that healthy bowels mean a healthy you. It can be an embarrassing topic but paying attention to your bowel movements is an important part of staying healthy. A healthy person should be excreting 3-4 bowel movements per day, and if that is not the case, you're probably constipated which can lead to many health concerns.

Here are a few things to get you started and on your way to a healthy colon

- Eat foods high in fiber such as apples, legumes, and flax and chia seeds.
- Drink apple cider vinegar: Dilute 1 tablespoon in 8 ounces of water.
- Eat cultured foods rich in probiotics like sauerkraut, kimchee, rejuvelac, or kefir.
- Get regular colonics, a process used by trained hydrotherapists to gently flush the colon. This process helps to loosen and eliminate toxic waste buildup.
- Consider taking a magnesium supplement which helps to break down fecal matter and assists cleansing your colon.
- Incorporate at home enemas into your routine.

90

- For 7 days, drink 1 tablespoon of psyllium husk and 1 tablespoon of bentonite clay mixed with 16 ounces of water. Drink lots of water during this time.

Detoxing the Liver

The liver is the largest internal organ and is responsible for breaking down and detoxifying substances in the body. The liver creates cholesterol and triglycerides. It works to metabolize carbohydrates and turns glucose into glycogen that is stored in the liver and muscle cells. The liver also produces bile that assists with the digestion of food. It works to help detoxify the body by converting ammonia (a compound created through the process of metabolism) into urea, which is expelled by the kidneys in the urine.

The liver works hard to break down medications, drugs, processed foods, alcohol, as well as insulin and other hormones produced by the body. It is also responsible for storing vitamins such as B12, folate, iron, Vitamin A, Vitamin D, and Vitamin K. According to *The Liver and Gallbladder Miracle Cleanse,* when there is a buildup of substances in the liver, it begins to overflow, stop functioning the way it is supposed to and wreaks havoc on other organs because it's no longer filtering out the toxins. Rather, it is spilling more toxins into your bloodstream. Over years of toxins bombarding the liver, gallstones begin to form. These gallstones block nutrients from being processed through the liver. These hardened gallstones block the liver from absorbing the nutrients your body needs to survive.

As you can see the liver has many functions and a tired liver can create fatigue, depression and many other ailments if it is not cared for and detoxed regularly.

How to Cleanse and Detoxify the Liver

Cleansing the liver is one of the most lifesaving actions you can take. Gallstones build up in the liver and gallbladder. Gallstones disturb the functioning of the liver, which has over 500 functions and impacts health in a major way. Doing a flush is one of the most important things you can do for your health. Cleansing your liver can heal many different illnesses that result from gallstones blockings the ducts which creates a backup in your system. By doing a liver/gallbladder cleanse (or a series of them), it can add years to your life, reverse or slow down the aging process and heal your body on a deeper, cellular level. By doing a series of these flushes you could potentially see amazing changes in your health. People have reported that they healed themselves of stubborn illnesses that they lived with for years!

Liver/Gallbladder Flush

- **Supplies you'll need:**

    o   4 cups of Organic Apple juice

    o   6 tsp of Malic Acid

    o   Stone Breaker by Herb Pharm

    o   125 drops of Phosfood by Standard Processing

    o   6 tbsp Apple Cider Vinegar, unfiltered with the 'mother'

    o   Epsom Salt

    o   1/2 cup Organic Extra Virgin, cold-pressed Olive Oil

    o   2 Fresh grapefruits

- **Directions**

    o   What to do 1 week before the cleanse
        - Eating clean for 6 days prior to the actual cleanse which means eat whole plant-based foods for 6 days which may include any vegetable, fruit, nut or seed and no dairy, animal protein, processed foods, caffeine, or sugar.

    o   For 6 days prior to the flush sip on 1 liter of water throughout the day mixed with:
        - 50 drops of Stone Breaker by Herb Pharm

92

- 125 drops of Phosfood by Standard Processing
- 1 tsp Malic Acid
- 1 tbsp apple cider vinegar

o On the day of the flush
- Eat a light breakfast consisting of steamed vegetables or oatmeal with a little bit of honey or fruit. DO NOT EAT ANY FAT, OIL, BUTTER, AVOCADO or PROTEIN.
- Do not eat lunch any later than 1:30 p.m.
- You may eat a lunch of fresh steamed veggies lightly seasoned with sea salt.

Your Cleansing Schedule:

2:00 p.m.: Mix 4 cups of organic apple juice and 4 tablespoons of Epsom salt to a quart mason jar. This makes four servings, 8 ounces each glass. Refrigerated concoction goes down a lot easier and tastes much better!

6:00 p.m.: Drink your first 8-ounce portion of the apple juice/Epsom salt mixture.

8:00 p.m.: Drink your second serving 8-ounce apple juice/Epsom salt mixture.

9:30 p.m.: If you have not had a bowel movement until now and have not done a colon cleanse within 24 hours, take a water enema; this will trigger a series of bowel movements.

9:45 p.m.: Wash the grapefruits and squeeze them by hand to obtain ¾ cup of juice. Discard any pulp you may have. Pour the grapefruit juice and ½ cup of olive oil into the mason jar. Close the jar tightly and shake hard until the solution becomes a watery substance.

10:00 p.m.: Stand next to your bed (do not sit down) and drink the olive oil/grapefruit mixture. Do not take more than 5 minutes for this. Lie down immediately on your right side for 30 minutes in fetal position. Do not get up during this time. You may also prepare a castor oil pack to place over your liver and an infrared heating pad can help the detoxification process, as well. After 30 minutes, you may go to sleep.

You may feel nauseous during the night and/or in the early morning hours. This is mostly due to a sudden outpouring of gallstones and toxins from the liver and gallbladder, pushing the oil mixture back into the stomach. The nausea will pass as the morning progresses.

The Following Morning

6:00-6:30 a.m.: Upon awakening, but not before 6 AM, drink your third 8-ounce glass of apple juice/Epsom Salt mixture. Continue to rest or go back to sleep. You may choose to do a water or coffee enema during this time as well.

8:00-8:30 a.m.: Drink your fourth and last 8-ounce glass of apple juice/Epsom Salt mixture

10:30 a.m.: You may drink freshly pressed fruit juice at this time. One half-hour later, you may eat one or two pieces of fresh fruit. One hour later you may eat a light snack. By the evening you should be back to normal and feel the first signs of improvement.

Note: There have been some conflicting opinions in the alternative medical field about this flush. I am providing this as information. Listen to your body to see if this is right for you. I provide what has worked for me and my clients.

Coffee Enemas

Incorporate the use of coffee enemas. This may sound like an odd and crazy thing to do when we're talking about anxiety and depression. This little secret to detoxification will help clear out what is no longer needed. Enemas have been around since ancient times and were fit for kings and queens. Dr. Max Gerson popularized the coffee enema through his work with cancer and tuberculosis patients in the late 1800's and early 1900's. He began to incorporate their use in his treatment and began to see miraculous healing results. Adding this to the protocol, he was able to assist people in detoxifying their bodies from the toxic buildup that cancer had created. So, what does this have to do with anxiety and depression? As you've learned, your liver builds up toxins which result in causing depression and anxiety. This enema will help support the release those toxins.

Coffee enemas work by entering the colon and reaching the hemorrhoidal vein and the portal system to the liver. Once in the liver, the coffee circulates through the liver to assist in removing toxins, parasites, yeasts, and other toxic buildup. It helps with the production of glutathione, the "master antioxidant" that our bodies produce, but decreases in production as we get older. The coffee increases bile flow from the liver, as well as the pancreas. It also allows the colon walls to become saturated and assists in helping to move waste that prevents absorption of nutrients. These are often used in alternative ways to heal cancer because there is so much toxic buildup. Drinking coffee does not produce the same effects.

Supplies Needed

- Enema bucket (preferably stainless steel)
- Organic whole bean light roasted coffee
- 4 cup measuring cup
- Coffee grinder
- Filtered water

Boil 3 cups of water and 2 tbsp. of ground organic coffee for 15 minutes on low heat. Strain coffee with a mesh strainer and keep the liquid. The water should boil down to about 2 to 2 ½ cups of coffee. Add another 1 ½ to 2 cups of cold water to cool the solution. Test the water with the back of your wrist (as you would baby formula) to make sure the solution is lukewarm and at body temperature.

Add the body temperature solution to your enema bucket. Go to the bathroom and lie on a comfortable towel on your right side (the side of your liver). Insert the tubing into your rectum and allow the solution to flow into your body. Once the solution has emptied out of the bucket, wait 15 minutes before expelling the liquid. Blood circulates through your liver every 3 minutes; therefore, the coffee solution will circulate up to 5 times during the 15 minutes.

Other Liver Loving Practices to Try

- Wake up with lemon water. Adding lemon to your water increases the bile flow of the liver and supports digestion and breaks down fat.
- Eat or drink the herbal teas such as dandelion greens, milk thistle and garlic.
- Drink fresh carrot and apple juice.
- Make parsley tea (recipe below)

All Over Cellular Detoxification

Liquid bentonite clay is one of my favorite products. It is made of volcanic ash and has a strong negative electromagnetic charge. When we drink the clay, it works like a magnet to pull the heavy metals and other toxins from the body. Your body does not absorb the clay, but as it moves through your body, the clay binds to toxins and pulls them out to be excreted. My favorite brand is Yerba Prima Bentonite, Detox Pint, 16 Ounce.

Spirulina and chlorella are two other favorites when I am going through a cleanse and in my daily routine. They are both considered superfoods and can be wonderful additions to your detox program and lifestyle. Chlorella is a single celled microalgae and spirulina is a multi-celled microalga. They are both known to bind to harmful toxins in your body such as pesticides, heavy metals, molds, chemicals and other toxins. They have been studied and shown to assist in the process of oxygenation, blood purification, support healthy blood pressure levels, boost your immune system, support weight loss, support cellular repair and growth, balance your body's pH, and energize your cells. Spirulina has a high ratio of protein and iron, as well as all eight essential amino acids, potassium, zinc, calcium, and vitamins B1, B2, B3,

B6 and B-12. Spirulina also has a high ratio of beta-carotene, while chlorella has a high level of chlorophyll (due to its dark green color).

Sample Detox Schedule

6:00 a.m. Wake up and greet the world! Give yourself a big beautiful hug and bring in the light
6:10 a.m. Drink 4oz coconut kefir
6:30 a.m. Yoga practice
7:00 a.m. Meditate for 10-20 minutes
7:20 a.m. Drink 12 to16 oz. lemon water
7:30 p.m. Prepare and take coffee enema
8:00 a.m. Drink 12 to-16 oz. carrot, apple, celery and ginger juice
8:30 a.m. Drink 1 cup of dandelion tea
9:00 a.m. Parsley tea. Sip throughout the day.
11:00 a.m. Watermelon Detox Delight
12:00 p.m. 1 cup of Vegetable Mineral Broth
2:00 p.m. Cucumber, Mint, Apple juice
4:00 p.m. Detoxifying Green Smoothie or Camu Camu smoothie
6:00 p.m. 1 cup of Vegetable Mineral broth
7:00 p.m. Meditate for 10 to20 minutes
8:00 p.m. Write in your Gratitude journal
9:00 p.m. Bedtime
 (See recipes below)

Detoxifying Recipes

Detoxifying Green Smoothie!

Need a little green in your day? Try blending your favorite greens into this green smoothie and you'll be amazed at how delicious this green drink really is! This smoothie has so many powerful nutrients that will not only supercharge your day but help detox your cells and revitalize your body.

Benefits of this Drink

Chamomile Tea: It supports wound healing, is an antioxidant, antibacterial. It is also known to help provide stress relief, promote relaxation and reduce muscle spasms, as well as support digestive health, restful sleep and healthy skin.

Granny Smith Apple: It is high in antioxidants, high in potassium which helps with cardiovascular health, anxiety and nervous system. It is in high fiber which helps you to stay full longer and helps to control blood sugar.

Lemon: It has immune boosting properties, balances pH in your body, flushes out toxins and helps to dissolve uric acid in body that can create joint pain and inflammation. It is also known to help to promote stress reducing effects.

Parsley: It is high in antioxidants, especially Vitamin C to help with free radicals, immune boosting support, cardiovascular support, helps to control blood pressure, and helps support weight loss.

Leafy Greens: Supports immune function, cancer prevention, supports eye health, supports bone health, and supports overall heart health.

Ginger: Best known for its medicinal benefits for relieving nausea and morning sickness. It can also be beneficial for reducing muscle pain, works as an anti-inflammatory, assists to lower risk of heart disease, cholesterol, and menstrual pain. It is also known to help fight infections and aids in the prevention of cancer.

Turmeric: This is a hot topic right now as many studies are coming out on the tremendous benefits of this root. It has been shown to help as a powerful anti-inflammatory, anti-depressant, assists in fighting cancer, and helps in the prevention of Alzheimer's.

Detoxifying Green Smoothie Recipe

1 cup of chamomile tea, cooled, or your favorite tea
1 Organic Granny Smith Apple, cut up
1/2 Organic lemon, peeled

1 big handful of organic parsley
1 big handful of organic cilantro
1 big handful of your favorite organic leafy green
1-inch fresh organic ginger
1-inch fresh organic turmeric
2 tsp. bee pollen

Place all ingredients in a blender of your choice, blend and enjoy!!!

Camu Camu Immune Boosting and Detoxifying Smoothie

Get your smoothie on with Camu Camu! Say what? This is a wonderful fruit that comes from the rain forests of Peru and Brazil. It has 60 times more vitamin C than an orange! Its scientific name is Myrciaria dubia, commonly known as camu camu, camucamu, cacari, or camocamo. This wonderful immune boosting small bushy tree tends to grow by river banks in the Amazon rain forest. It produces reddish purple fruit similar to a cherry.

Benefits of Camu Camu

- Powerful antioxidant: 60 times more vitamin C than an orange!
- Immune booster: Boosts your immune system to help you stay healthy and fight off infection.
- Anti-inflammatory: Vitamin c assists in decreasing inflammation in the body.
- Helps brain function: Can alleviate depression and improve mood.
- Protects against free-radicals (created from stress, environmental toxins, inflammation, etc.): Vitamin C fights free-radicals in the body.

Next time you're at your local health food store look for this powder to add to your morning smoothie for an extra immune boosting treat for your body!

Camu Camu Immune Boosting and Detoxifying Smoothie Recipe

1 1/2 c Purified or filtered water
1/4 c of Organic Blueberries
1 tbsp. Hemp hearts
1 tbsp. Flax seeds
1 tbsp. Chlorella
1 tbsp. Camu Camu
1 Banana
5 kale leaves (de-stemmed)
1 Scoop or empty a couple of probiotic capsules.
1 dash of cayenne pepper to taste

Place all ingredients in a blender or Nutribullet until kale leaves are pureed.

Morning Wake Up Call Juice

3 Organic Carrots
1 Organic Granny Smith apple
3 ribs of organic celery
1-inch fresh organic ginger

Throw all ingredients in a juicer. Drink immediately.
Parsley Tea

Boil a quart of water and remove from heat. Place a bunch of organic parsley in the water and allow to steep for 2 to 3 hours.

Add lemon or mint for extra flavor. May interfere with blood thinning medications due to the level of vitamin K

Watermelon Detox Delight
(makes a big batch)

¼ of whole watermelon or 1 small watermelon
6 inches of peeled fresh organic ginger
2 Organic Granny smith apples
16 oz. Aloe Vera juice

2 organic limes, peeled
Several handfuls of different organic greens, such as kale, bok choy, spinach, arugula, etc.

Throw everything in a blender and blend until smooth.

Vegetable Mineral Broth

- 4-5 small organic garlic cloves, finely chopped
- 1 Knob of organic ginger, finely chopped
- 1 Organic purple onion, chopped
- 1 Organic leek, finely chopped
- 1 Organic fennel bulb
- 2 Organic celery sticks, chopped
- 2 Organic carrots, chopped
- 1 small organic beet, chopped
- 1 Organic jalapeño, diced
- 3 cups of organic greens such as kale, spinach, or collards, etc.
- 6 cups of filtered water, or to cover ingredients.
- 1 tbsp. apple cider vinegar, with the "mother"
- 2, 4-inch pieces of kombu
- 1 cup dried mushrooms such as shiitake, trumpet or oyster, etc.
- 2 tsp. turmeric powder
- ½ cup fresh organic parsley leaves
- Celtic sea salt, to taste
- Black pepper, to taste

1. Add onion, garlic and ginger to large soup pot and enough water to cook onions until translucent
2. Add the rest of the ingredients, except the greens, bring to a boil and then simmer with the lid on for 1 hour (or more).
- Once the soup has cooked, add in the fresh greens at the end and keep them bright and colorful.
- Enjoy!

Cucumber Mint Apple Juice

1 Organic cucumber

1 handful of Organic mint
1 Organic Granny Smith Apple
1-inch fresh organic ginger

Throw all of the ingredients into a juicer and enjoy!

Take some time to thank yourself for honoring your body and starting where you are. Remember, this is a journey and being gentle with yourself is the most loving gift you can give to yourself.

CHAPTER SEVEN

Other Considerations for Healing

Look deep into nature, and then you will understand everything better. ~ Albert Einstein

Essential Oils

Essential oils have been used for thousands of years as plant medicine for many ailments and concerns. They are a highly concentrated form of the plant and are used in small doses. They can be used topically, aromatically, or ingested. Due to the high level of potency, it is important to know how to use them and which one is best in what form. For the purpose of this book, I'll discuss using them topically and aromatically to help manage anxiety and depression. For aromatherapy, I suggest getting a diffuser to disperse the essential oils into your environment. For applying topically, I suggest getting a carrier oil such as fractionated coconut oil, almond oil, or jojoba oil. Carrier oils are important due to the strong nature of the essential oils, and some essential oils should not be put directly on the skin. It is important to find a reputable company when purchasing essential oils. Many oils sold in stores are mixed with artificial ingredients, diluted to be non-effective, and sourced inorganically. Pure, organic essential oils can have a profound effect on mood, sleep and overall wellbeing. The olfactory system detects the oil molecules and interacts with the nervous system to assist in creating calm or uplifting moods, depending on the oil.

Essential Oils for Anxiety and Depression

Lavender Essential Oil

This is an oil that creates peace and tranquility. When used topically or aromatically, it enters the blood stream or accesses the emotional center of the brain, the amygdala, and has a very profound calming effect. Add 2 to 3 drops to a tablespoon of carrier oil and rub it on your temples, back of your wrists and/or the bottom of your feet. Try rubbing it on your wrists or around your ears to access the calmness and relaxation acupressure points. Add a couple drops to your diffuser and breathe in the beautiful scent of lavender.

Ylang Ylang Essential Oil

This is another great stress reliever and affects your nervous system through inhalation or when used topically. Try diffusing this oil in the air or mix 2 to 3 drops with 1 tablespoon of carrier oil and rub it on your temples, back of wrists and/or bottom of your feet.

Frankincense Essential Oil

This oil has so many uses, and it can be used for both anxiety and depression. It is known for uplifting mood and increasing peace. Try diffusing it in the air and breathing in the aroma or mix 2 to 3 drops with 1 tablespoon of carrier oil and apply it to your temples, back of wrists and/or bottom of your feet.

Rose Essential Oil

This will promote a sense of peace and overall wellbeing. As mentioned earlier in the book, rose has a high vibration of 320 MHz which can assist in raising your vibration to promote a sense of joy and self-worth. Try diffusing it into the air or mix 2 to 3 drops with 1 tablespoon of carrier oil and rub it on your wrists or around your ears to access the acupressure points for uplifting mood.

Orange Essential Oil

Part of the citrus family and known for its anti-depressant effects. Diffuse a couple drops of this aromatically or dilute 2 to 3 drops with 1 tablespoon of carrier oil and add to bathwater or rub under your nose.

Clary Sage Essential Oil

This oil is known for its positive effects on levels of dopamine, which uplifts your mood. It can be used for both anxiety and depression. Try diffusing this in the air, inhaling deeply, or mix 2 to 3 drops with 1 tablespoon of carrier oil and apply it to your wrists, massage it into your ears, bottom of your feet, or around your pillow at night to promote restful sleep.

Connecting With the Earth

Getting out into Nature is vital to wellness and vitality. Scientific research shows the value of being in Nature; it is essential for our body, mind and spirit. According to earthing.com, Earth has a magnetic pull that literally grounds us by transmitting electrons through our feet when we walk barefoot outside.

In today's society, we have gotten so far away from Nature. We are surrounded by walls and we spend our time working inside under florescent lights. We wear shoes all day long. All of these things separate us from being close to Nature. When we are disconnected from Nature on a consistent basis, it causes emotional discord, fatigue, low energy, anxiety, depression and other dis-eases. Think about when you get flooded with emotions. You become uncentered, ungrounded and may feel like you're out of your body or disconnected from it. Connecting to

Earth will help ground your energy (remember emotions are energy in emotion). The energy from Earth helps us regain our energy, vitality and overall feeling of being grounded.

Grounding Exercise

- o   Go outside, whether in your front lawn, at a park nearby, the beach or mountains.
- o   Take off your shoes and socks.
- o   Feel the ground beneath you.
- o   Imagine a light is coming in from the top of your head and moving all the way down your body. As this light reaches your feet, imagine roots growing from your feet, all the way down to the center of Earth. Imagine the roots and light reach the center of Earth and connect with the strongest grounding vibration. Imagine this energy pulsating its way back up to you through your feet. Imagine this light circling around from your feet to the center of Earth. Just feel the grounded energy you are receiving.

Sleep and Your Nighttime Z's

Sleep is probably the most important factor in managing wellness and overall emotional and physical health. This is something that gets taken for granted or devalued in our society. When Sally first came to me, she was averaging 4-5 hours of sleep per night. Her reasoning was, "I'll sleep later, when I retire." She also complained that she couldn't sleep or woke up in the middle of the night, unable to get back to sleep. Unfortunately, this is a common problem for many people. More and more people are prescribed medications to help fall and stay asleep. The problem with this is it's not getting to the root of the problem. Sleep issues can stem from a lot of different possibilities, such as unresolved stress and trauma, poor sleeping environment, diet, caffeine consumption, etc. Sleep is a time when your body is healing and repairing itself. It can't do that if you're not getting the adequate amount of sleep you need. Following the protocols in this book will help you with your sleep cycles.

Sleep Cycles

There's not a lot of agreement in the area of good sleep hygiene, the right number of hours, or when to sleep. I typically like to go with an Ayurvedic approach based on the information found at mapi.com. Ayurveda is the science of life, is a medical system that promotes the understanding of the mind-body connection and is based on the work developed by sages in India. This system states that we have 3 different constitutions, or doshas, Kapha, Pitta, and Vata-within the cycles of the body, time of day and the earth. Kapha is known as dense and heavy energy which occurs around 6:00 a.m. to 10:00 a.m. and 6:00 p.m. to 10:00 p.m. Pitta is known as fiery energy and occurs 10:00 a.m. to 2:00 p.m. and 10:00 p.m. and 2:00 a.m. Vata is known as airy energy which occurs from 2:00 a.m. to 6:00 a.m. and 2:00 p.m. to 6:00 p.m. With these cycles in mind, when we go to bed between 9:30 p.m. and 10:00 p.m., we experience a sleep cycle of the heavier energy that makes us sleep. However, if we stay up past 10:00 p.m., we often get a second surge of energy which results in difficulty sleeping. Try getting into the habit of going to bed at 9:30 p.m. and waking up at 6:00 a.m. and see what happens.

Other Sleep Considerations

Don'ts

o Don't drink caffeine past 3:00 p.m. or 12:00 p.m. if you're sensitive to it.
o Don't use your cell phone as an alarm clock.
o Don't watch TV, news or anything else stimulating at least 2-3 hours before bed.
o Don't eat within 2 hours before bed, as your body will focus on digesting and not resting.

Do's

o Turn off all lights, including computer monitors.
o Get an old-fashioned alarm clock.
o Read something light.
o Write in your gratitude journal.

o Drink herbal tea about an hour before bedtime, such as chamomile, tulsi (holy basil), lemon balm or lavender teas.

o Take a warm bath with Epsom salt and a few drops of lavender essential oil which help to relax the muscles.

⊖ Do a bedtime meditation or breathing exercise. Breathe in through your nose to the count of four, hold at the top of your breath for the count of four, breathe out to the count of four and hold for the count of four. Do this breathing exercise 10 times. As you are doing this breathing practice, imagine your body is falling softly into the bed and you're in control of your body. Invite it to relax and gently fall asleep. You can change the number count, if four is not enough for you. Listen to your body for what feels right.

Supplements and Herbs

Sometimes taking supplements until you start feeling better is necessary. Listen to your body for what feels right. Here is a list of some of my favorite herbs and supplements that complement the work you are doing in this book. Understand that it is just that, a complement to all the other practices presented in this book. Many of these herbs are adaptogens which are a group of plants that help the body adapt to chemical, physical and environmental stresses.

Ashwagandha

This is an adaptogenic herb used in Ayurveda medicine. It has been traditionally prescribed for many ailments but is mostly known for its ability to lower the stress hormone cortisol and create a sense of overall calmness. You can find this in tea, capsules or powdered form.

Holy Basil or Tulsi

This is another adaptogenic herb used in the Ayurvedic tradition to help relieve stress, anxiety and even has an anti-depressant effect. You can find this in tea, tincture or capsule form.

Rhodiola

This an adaptogenic herb is also known to help reduce the symptoms of stress and anxiety by lowering the stress hormone cortisol and reducing the fight or flight response. It also decreases depression by improving brain function. You can find this in tincture, tea or capsule form.

Magnesium

There has been a lot of talk in the health world about how magnesium deficient many people are. When there is a deficiency in magnesium, energy cannot be produced or used in the cells, muscles cannot efficiently relax, and contract and hormones cannot synthesize to properly support body functions. Magnesium has been shown play a vital role in prevention of disease. It is suggested that a deficiency is linked to depression and anxiety. Just think about when you are stressed or anxious and struggle to relax your body, it may be due to a magnesium deficiency. Research shows that incorporating magnesium may decrease symptoms of anxiety, depression and may help you sleep better. Try magnesium orotate for maximum absorption or eat more magnesium rich foods.

Foods that have the highest amount of magnesium include:

Food	Magnesium	Amount
Almonds	80mg	1oz
Spinach	157mg	1 cup
Pumpkin Seeds	184mg	¼ cup
Avocado	58mg	1 avocado
Dark chocolate	64mg	1oz
Black beans	120mg	1 cup
Buckwheat	65mg	1oz
Banana	37mg	1 banana

Movement and Exercise

There is so much research that shows the benefits of exercise on the brain and how it decreases both anxiety and depression. According to a recent study done by UCLA, exercise has been shown to increase growth factors and assist in the regeneration of neural networks. These networks allow us to create new behaviors and feelings. Another study out of Stockholm has shown that exercise has an anti-depressant effect and is responsible for cell growth in the hippocampus, the part of the brain that is responsible for learning and memory. Another study reported findings that indicate exercise activates the central opioid system by increasing endorphins (the feel-good hormones), "a mechanism and a potential therapeutic role for exercise are suggested for treatment of pain, alcoholism, anxiety, bulimia, hypertension, addiction, depression, and anorexia nervosa".

There is evidence that is now coming to light that shows living a sedentary lifestyle has the potential for causing long-term, negative health effects. So, with all the evidence pointing toward the positive health effects of exercise, how much movement are you getting? Sometimes, we know something might be good for us, but we don't do it.

When Sally came to me, she was not exercising at all. In fact, she wasn't using her gym membership. She had a bike but wasn't using that either. We discussed this, and she said things like, "I don't have time" or "I'm too tired." All these beliefs were true for her and served to shape her thinking about exercise. When we started talking about the value of exercise and what it could do to help her feel better emotionally, physically and spiritually her thinking began to change. We discussed how starting small and building from there would be most beneficial for her. So, Sally started out on her bike with her son riding in his baby cart on the back; she rode her bike around a 1-mile block. She did this for about a month. She started to feel stronger and less tired. She also realized that she had the time and energy for exercise. She then stretched it to cycling 10 miles and then 20 miles within a few months. And then one day, she decided to enter an organized bike ride for charity. She signed up to ride 100 miles! With this goal in mind, Sally trained 6 months for the event. To her surprise and delight, she found the time to train and continued to feel the benefits of exercising. She was feeling elated after each workout, her mood improved, her anxiety decreased, and she felt more productive and she even lost some weight. She found a love for cycling long distances. She experienced the present moment as she rode the hills in her area. She showed up on the day of the charity ride, rode her heart out and gave it her all. Today, Sally continues to love to ride her bike and knows that when she stretches her limits of what she believes is possible, she'll achieve her goals.

Ways to Embrace Exercise

No matter where you are starting out with exercise, I invite you to do the following:

- o Start out small. Try walking around the block at lunch time, after work or early in the morning.
- o Set a goal for yourself. Find an event you can work toward, such as a 5k walk/run, ride for charity, or a hike in the mountains.
- o Discover what kind of exercise you enjoy. Maybe swimming is something you prefer, or racquetball, softball, crossfit, etc. There are so many different types of exercise. The point is to move your body in a way that feels right to you.
- o If you work at a desk or sedentary job, get up once every hour and stretch and move your body.

Yoga

Yoga could be placed in the exercise category, but for the purpose of this book and the amazing benefits it has for anxiety and depression, I felt that it was important enough to be in its own discussion topic. Yoga has been around for over 2000 years and has been most recently studied for its positive effect on stress, anxiety and depression.

The most common form of yoga practiced in the west is called Hatha. This typically focuses on physical movement and various poses, called asanas, while being mindful of your breath, called pranayama. It usually ends with a final relaxation/meditation pose called savasana. There is a sequence of poses each instructor will take you through, inviting you to breathe along the way. It creates space to open up within ourselves and allow new energy in. Some yoga instructors will invite you to create an intention before the session and be mindful of that intention throughout the session. This helps to stay focused on your goal through the yoga practice.

Breathing is essential to our well-being, as this connects us to our lifeforce energy, chi or prana and allows it to move through our bodies, releasing all the energy that is stagnant and stuck. Pairing breathing with movement creates the energy flow on a deeper level. It allows the cells to begin to clear and allows us to feel deeply and heal. When you tune into places in your body that feel stuck or tense you are consciously moving stagnant energy and creating new energy.

You may think you need to be limber and "bendy" to do yoga. This is not the case. Anyone can do yoga. Yoga is a gentle process and really honors the person on the mat. It's about learning to not judge yourself or compare yourself to others. It's about learning to let go of any desire to be anyone other than yourself. It creates a space for accepting yourself where are right now. Yoga is about finding your center and learning to be present. It's about listening to your body and what is right for you.

I invite you to find a yoga class in your area or find a video online.

CHAPTER EIGHT

Your Empowered Soul

There are no extra pieces in the universe. Everyone is here because he or she has a place to fill, and every piece must fit itself into the big jigsaw puzzle. ~Deepak Chopra

One day, Sally was meditating and something profound happened. During her meditation, a feeling of calm, and yet, intense gratitude came over her. She opened her eyes and looked around the room. Instead of seeing her room in the same way as she had when she closed her eyes, she awoke to a brand-new experience. As she explained it to me, she looked around the room and realized she was looking out of her eyes through the eyes of her soul. It was as if she was waking up to her soul and for the first time experiencing being in a body. She was overcome with joy, love and gratitude for all that she had. She began to cry out of pure bliss for the experience that brought her here. That was true gratitude. She witnessed it more deeply than she had ever felt it before. It was at that moment she realized her mission on this planet. She was here to fulfill a purpose and she was going to manifest all of her heart's desires.

As Sally applied all of the principles in this book, she began to feel clear minded, her energy started to soar, and she was happier than she had ever been. Her anxiety and depression lifted and she finally felt like she was able to operate at a much higher frequency. She recognized that her body was becoming a clear vessel to give and receive the messages her soul was sending her. She was able to work together with her soul, rather than fighting against herself. As Sally cleared her mind of thoughts and emotions that were not serving her and changed the way she viewed herself and others, her life began to shift and change in ways she could not believe. Sally began to open up the channels of receiving. As she changed her diet and only consumed food that were of the highest vibrational frequency, she realized that her mind and body were also vibrating at a higher frequency. She noticed that if she went off course and ate something her body wasn't used to or didn't like, her body would speak to her through fatigue, foggy mind or anger and sadness. She realized that the energy of the foods she consumed had everything to do with how she felt. By choosing only high vibrating thoughts, emotions, food, and relationships, she recognized the profound spiritual awakening that was happening simultaneously.

Manifesting

Sally recognized that life wasn't happening *to* her anymore. Instead, she began to wake up to her potential and her power as a human being. She began co-creating her life's plan. As a contributor, she made things happen. She fully understood and embraced what it meant to be a spiritual being, having a human experience. These weren't just fluffy words that felt good to say; she began to fully embrace this concept. Sally had been afraid to want because she was afraid she couldn't have the things she most wanted in life. She began to recognize that it's ok to want things in life and have a say in her future. She realized she didn't have to make others happy. She realized that she mattered, too. She could have the life that she always thought was for "other" people. One of her beliefs that we uncovered and worked on was "I don't deserve the things I want." Through affirmations and EFT/Tapping, we cleared the energy that held that belief in place. Amazing shifts started happening. She began to envision what her dream life could look like. This process was exciting for her because she was actually giving herself permission to dream about the kind of job she wanted, the home, travel, and how much money she wanted to make. Through this process, Sally created another vision board. Remember the vision board you created in Chapter One?

Changing her job was the first thing she decided to work on. She really wanted to make a living doing something that she loved. She wanted freedom in her schedule and she wanted to double her income by the end of the year (it was September). We discussed being in alignment with her soul's truth and her values, particularly freedom. She focused on the feeling associated with having the job of her dreams by creating the feeling of freedom within her soul. She knew she was on the right track because the excitement ran through her body. As sometimes happens when we start down the pathway toward manifesting our desires, the old feelings of anxiety and depression returned and she felt off-centered when she listened to the fears her ego brought up. The fears she experienced were similar to what we discussed in Chapter 3 on thoughts. When your soul speaks to you, it comes through feeling alive and excited. It feels right. It wants to help you achieve all that you want. It might feel scary at times, but your soul will never steer you wrong. When you are in alignment with your truth and purpose, synchronicities emerge. The right people, places and events show up to support you and your mission. This happens when you become absolutely clear. When you are fearful or anxious, you send the universe unclear messages and it doesn't understand what you want because you aren't focusing on the feeling you want to manifest. Instead, you're focused on what you don't want. Sometimes, it may not feel like the universe is showing up at all. The universe will always provide what you need for your highest good. There may be a lesson or two to learn before you manifest exactly what you want. These lessons will keep coming up until we "get it". You might wonder why the same relationship problems keep happening. What is the lesson? It's not that you always choose horrible partners. By taking an empowered approach, you step out of the victim mode and ask yourself "What is the lesson?" and "How can I grow?"

So, Sally focused on freedom and started getting good at noticing when those fear-based thoughts came up. She meditated on what it would feel like to double her income and what she would be doing when she had her dream job. She meditated on this for 10 minutes a day and then, she let it go. One day, about 3 months after she began this process, she was looking at her email and found a job announcement in her inbox. It looked like a good opportunity, so she sent in her résumé. Within 10 minutes, she received an email offering her an interview. The interview went well, and she was offered a 2nd interview and then, they offered her the job! Not only was this a job that gave her the opportunity to do something she loved, the pay was double her current salary. That meant she could cut back on her hours and experience the freedom she so valued. This happened during the last week in December! Her soul was in alignment with her highest potential and the universe was working with her to create her vision. Life wasn't working against her. When she showed up and knew what she wanted, worked with her soul and the universal energies, she became a co-creator in her own life. She was not a victim, but a victor over the circumstances of her life.

Manifest Your Reality

Before you begin, I invite you to do a heart-focused breathing exercise. Start by placing your hand over your heart as you breathe and direct your focus to your heart. As you breathe in, imagine you are doing so through your heart, and, as you breathe out, imagine it is through your heart. Do this 3 times. This will center you and allow space to receive the answers.

1. Ask yourself: What do I want? Sometimes, it is easier to ask. "what don't I want?" because then you can clear out what you don't really want and discover what is at your heart and soul's desire.
2. What does it look like? How will you know when you have what you want? Create a Vision Board for this. Refer to Chapter One for Vision Board instructions.
3. How will it feel? It's not the object that you're really after, it's the feeling. Do you want the feeling of freedom, security, or excitement? What feeling will your vision give you?

117

4. Write it all down and create a symbol for your vision.

5. Meditate for 10 minutes. Envision your dreams becoming a reality by imagining the picture or the symbol and remembering the feeling you will have once you get what you desire.

6. If you notice any resistance, notice where the resistance is coming from and use the EFT/Tapping exercise and then create an Affirmation on Fire for the limiting belief (Chapters 2 and 3)

7. Be grateful now for what you want. Feel the gratitude radiating through your soul. Act as if you have already manifested your desire.

8. You are now aligned with your soul and showing your soul and the universe an exact picture of what you want. Watch miracles happen!

Another shift was occurring within Sally. She realized that everything that happened outside was a reflection of what was within. Her soul projected her ego's thoughts and beliefs onto others. She saw this though the eyes of her soul and when she began to really love herself and who she was, she began to see others with that same love. Once she awoke to this realization, she was able to recognize that everyone on the planet is here to serve a purpose. She could choose to separate herself from their "stuff", not take their actions personally and send them love instead. Because she was learning to stand in her truth, she understood that other people had their own path to follow and everyone was doing the very best they could. When she began to view people as love and spiritual beings working to accomplish their own mission for being on the planet, she was able to have more compassion for others. She realized that everyone is ONE human consciousness and when one of us evolves, we all evolve. It is for the greatest good to support and love each other. There is no separation.

There is no separation. What does this mean? The way we live and breathe affects every other being. Lynne McTaggart has demonstrated this time and time again through her Intention Experiments. Through field work, she has proven that thought affects physical reality. She has illustrated that our thoughts, or consciousness,

118

not only affect ourselves, but those around us. Our thoughts and intentions can harm or help heal ourselves, others and the world. The power of meditation, prayer and conscious thought is nothing short of miraculous. When we sit with focused thought it can have powerful effects in our lives and when a group sits with a specific thought or intention, the effects are compounded, As Lynne depicted in her book, *The Intention Experiment,* through group intention, peace was invoked in Sri Lanka, seeds germinated, and a 10-year post 9/11 peace experiment resulted in fewer war casualties and attacks, and more love and compassion from those involved in the experiment from all over the world. Another example, is the Maharishi Effect. Maharishi Mahesh Yogi brought Transcendental Meditation (TM) to the West in the 1960's. From 1979-1985, a group of TM meditators met to create coherence throughout the entire world. Their progress was observed, and it was reported that there was a significant reduction in the number of violent deaths including homicides, suicides, and traffic fatalities. These experiments have been repeated with similar results.

When we come from a heart centered place, focused on gratitude, abundance, freedom, or love we impact those around us by the energy we emit. The body becomes coherent and changes our mind and body so they become synchronized. It allows us to move out of victimhood and into living our true, highest potential for living our soul's purpose. The planet needs you to invoke the love that is your birthright and to extend it to others.

When understanding how integral you are to this world and those around you, you also understand the role you play on the planet. How can you use this insight in your life? Look out from your soul to the eyes of others and see within them. See them as beautiful souls and send them love, no matter who they are. When we send out love, we will get love back. Love is powerful force and can change anything instantaneously. There are really only two emotions, love and fear. Everything else stems from these. Which one are you going to choose? As Anais Nin so eloquently said, "We don't see the world as it is, we see it as we are."

Universal Love Energy

119

As you set out on the path to heal from anxiety or depression or both, I invite you to stop and pay attention to your voice. When you learn to *really* honor yourself by taking the time to embrace the philosophies and practice the exercises in this book, changes will naturally occur. When you believe that your voice matters in the world, you start to connect with your deeper purpose and remember why you are here. What do you want to create? Re-visit your answers in Chapter One for a refresher. Have they changed? Take some time and answer the questions again. We are always growing and evolving. When you stifle or ignore your voice you may feel anxiety and depression, and feel out of balance. Learning to love yourself and align with your true worth allows you to see the world from a different, more loving perspective. We are all made from love, and you are no exception. You are a beautiful soul with a deep purpose. When you show up for yourself and give to yourself in the ways that are laid out in this book, you will manifest the greatness that you already are. I invite you to see yourself as divine love. Choose to believe that the world is open to you and all that you wish to create.

Universal Love Exercise

Take a moment and breathe into your body. Gently close your eyes and find your center. Take a deep breath in through your nose and out through your mouth and imagine that breath going right into your heart center. Now open your eyes and see the world from your soul. Imagine opening your eyes for the first time on this earth plane and looking at your surroundings from your soul. Through the eyes of your soul, find that curiosity, awe and gratitude for being here. Imagine you are a magnet and you magnetize all that love toward you. Know that love energy is abundant, expansive and infinite. When you connect to your soul, send your humanness love and beauty and find compassion for yourself and all that you have experienced. Remember, it is all in service of a deeper purpose. Then send that love to your friends and family, your neighbors, the city or town that you're in, move that love out to your country, and then embrace the world and universe with that love. See yourself outside of Earth and the universe. Send love and embrace everything with a beautiful hug. You are more powerful than you imagine. By extending that love and light, you are touching Earth with your love and raising the vibration of the world (and beyond). You are an Empowered Soul.

References

Any Anxiety Disorder. (n.d.). Retrieved July 1, 2018, from

   https://www.nimh.nih.gov/health/statistics/any-anxiety-

   disorder.shtml

Berger, J. (2015, November 24). Ayurvedic Time and Balanced Sleep

   | Maharishi Ayurveda Blog. Retrieved September 1, 2018, from

   http://www.mapi.com/blog/ayurvedic-time-and-balanced-

   sleep.html

Bjørnebekk, A., Mathé, A. A., & Brené, S. (2005, September). The

   antidepressant effect of running is associated with increased

   hippocampal cell proliferation. Retrieved August 1, 2018, from

   https://www.ncbi.nlm.nih.gov/pubmed/15769301

Braverman, E. R. (2005). *The edge effect achieve total health and

   longevity with the balanced brain advantage*. New York.: Sterling

   Publishing Company.

Brogan, K. (2018, April 26). From Gut to Brain: The Inflammation-

   Depression Connection. Retrieved October 14, 2018, from

   https://kellybroganmd.com/from-gut-to-brain-the-inflammation-

   connection/

Brown, B. (2015). *Daring greatly: How the courage to be vulnerable transforms the way we live, love, parent, and lead*. New York, NY: Avery.

Coherence. (2012, November 11). Retrieved October 13, 2018, from https://www.heartmath.org/articles-of-the-heart/the-math-of-heartmath/coherence/

Dice, K., & Benigas, S. (2015). *Plant Base Nutrition Quick Start Guide*[FNL]. The Plantrician Project.

DISPENZA, D. J. (2019). *BECOMING SUPERNATURAL: How common people are doing the uncommon*. S.l.: HAY HOUSE UK.

Earthing.com. (n.d.). Retrieved August 1, 2018, from https://www.earthing.com/

Emmons, R. (2010, November 16). Why Gratitude Is Good. Retrieved July 1, 2018, from https://greatergood.berkeley.edu/article/item/why_gratitude_is_good

Environmental Working Group. (n.d.). Dirty Dozen™ Fruits and Vegetables with the Most Pesticides. Retrieved July 1, 2018, from https://www.ewg.org/foodnews/dirty-dozen.php

Environmental Working Group. (n.d.). Clean Fifteen™ Conventional

Produce with the Least Pesticides. Retrieved July 1, 2018, from

https://www.ewg.org/foodnews/clean-fifteen.php

FAO Calls on World Governments to Encourage Sustainable, Plant-

Based Protein as Impact of Meat and Dairy Soar. (2018, January

22). Retrieved July 1, 2018, from

http://www.onegreenplanet.org/news/fao-calls-on-governments-

to-encourage-sustainable-plant-based-protein/

Goodland, R., & Anhang, J. (n.d.). Livestock and Climate Change.

Retrieved from http://www.worldwatch.org/node/6294

Greger, M. (2017). *How not to die*. Place of publication not

identified: Pan Books.

Gut Health Project. (2017, November 30). Home. Retrieved October

1, 2018, from https://www.guthealthproject.com/20-pounds-of-

poop/

Hadhazy, A. (2010, February 12). Think Twice: How the Gut's

"Second Brain" Influences Mood and Well-Being. Retrieved

October 1, 2018, from

https://www.scientificamerican.com/article/gut-second-brain/

Harvard Health Publishing. (n.d.). Understanding Inflammation.

Retrieved October 14, 2018, from

https://www.health.harvard.edu/staying-healthy/understanding-

inflammation

Health Benefits of Magnesium. (n.d.). Retrieved October 15, 2018,

from https://www.ancient-minerals.com/magnesium-

benefits/health/

Heart-Focused Breathing. (2012, August 20). Retrieved July 1, 2018,

from https://www.heartmath.org/articles-of-the-heart/the-math-of-

heartmath/heart-focused-breathing/

Hidden in Plain Sight. (2018, April 27). Retrieved July 1, 2018, from

http://sugarscience.ucsf.edu/hidden-in-plain-

sight/#.W7wKWRNKhZ0

Kefir vs. Yogurt. (n.d.). Retrieved from http://www.kefir.net/kefir-vs-

yogurt/

Knüppel, A., Shipley, M. J., Llewellyn, C. H., & Brunner, E. J.

(2017, July 27). Sugar intake from sweet food and beverages,

common mental disorder and depression: Prospective findings

from the Whitehall II study. Retrieved July 1, 2018, from

https://www.nature.com/articles/s41598-017-05649-7

Knüppel, A., Shipley, M. J., Llewellyn, C. H., & Brunner, E. J.

(2017, July 27). Sugar intake from sweet food and beverages,

common

mental disorder and depression: Prospective findings from the

Whitehall II study. Retrieved July 1, 2018, from

https://www.ncbi.nlm.nih.gov/pmc/articles/PMC5532289/

Lenoir, M., Serre, F., Cantin, L., & Ahmed, S. H. (2007, August 1).

Intense Sweetness Surpasses Cocaine Reward. Retrieved July 1,

2018, from

https://www.ncbi.nlm.nih.gov/pmc/articles/PMC1931610/

Lipski, E. (2012). *Digestive wellness: Strengthen the immune system*

and prevent disease through healthy digestion. New York, NY:

McGraw-Hill.

McTaggart, L. (n.d.). *Living the Field: Directed Intention*[PDF].

McTaggart, L. (2013). *The intention experiment: Using your thoughts*

to change your life and the world. New York: Atria Paperback.

Molteni, R., Zheng, J. Q., Ying, Z., Gómez-Pinilla, F., & Twiss, J. L.

(2004, June 01). Voluntary exercise increases axonal regeneration from sensory neurons. Retrieved August 1, 2018, from

https://www.ncbi.nlm.nih.gov/pubmed/15159540

Moritz, A. (2007). *The liver and gallbladder miracle cleanse: An all-natural, at-home flush to purify and rejuvenate your body.*

Berkeley, CA: Ulysses Press.

Mu, Q., Kirby, J., Reilly, C. M., & Luo, X. M. (2017). Retrieved

September 1, 2018, from

https://www.ncbi.nlm.nih.gov/pmc/articles/PMC5440529/ leaky

gut

Neff, K. (n.d.). Definition and Three Elements of Self Compassion |

Kristin Neff. Retrieved October 10, 2018, from https://self-compassion.org/the-three-elements-of-self-compassion-2/

Neff, K. (2015, June 10). Self-Compassion Exercise 1: How would

you treat a friend? Retrieved July 1, 2018, from https://self-compassion.org/exercise-1-treat-friend/

Organic Standards. (n.d.). Retrieved July 1, 2018, from

https://www.ams.usda.gov/grades-standards/organic-standards

Owen, N., Sparling, P. B., Healy, G. N., Dunstan, D. W., &

Matthews, C. E. (2010, December). Retrieved August 1, 2018,

from https://www.ncbi.nlm.nih.gov/pmc/articles/PMC2996155/

Sedentary lifestyle

Owens, K., Feldman, J., & Kepner, J. (2010). *Wide Range of Diseases Linked to Pesticides*[PDF]. A quarterly publication of Beyond Pesticides.

Psychiatric Drugs: Create Violence and Suicide[PDF]. (2018, March). Los Angeles: Citizens Commission on Human Rights International A Mental Health Industry Watchdog.

Robbins, A. (1991). *Awaken the Giant Within: How to Take Immediate Control of Your Mental, Emotional, Physical and Financial Destiny!*Free Press.

Robbins, A. (1992). *Anthony Robbins Living Health*[CD]. San Diego: Robbins Research International.

STRAUS, H. (2009). *DR MAX GERSON: Healing the hopeless*. S.l.: TOTALITY BOOKS.

Vital Signs. (2018, June 11). Retrieved June 15, 2018, from https://www.cdc.gov/vitalsigns/suicide/index.html

Walker, N. W. (2009). *Colon health: The key to a vibrant life!*Boise, ID: Norwalk.

Welcome to IFIC Foundation. (n.d.). Retrieved June 1, 2018, from

    https://www.foodinsight.org/

Zimmermann, K. A. (2018, February 20). Lymphatic System: Facts,

    Functions & Diseases. Retrieved June 1, 2018, from

    https://www.livescience.com/26983-lymphatic-system.html

About the Author

Stacy is a spiritual being. She continues to follow her soul mission and work as a psychotherapist, health and wellness coach and author. She has a passion for integrating spirituality, nutrition and energy modalities into her work to support the whole person. She received her master's and bachelor's from Colorado State University in Social Work and pursued her health coaching training from the Institute for Integrative Nutrition. She is trained in Eye Movement Desensitization and Reprocessing (EMDR) and Emotional Freedom Techniques (EFT/Tapping). She has been teaching people meditation and soul connection techniques in her practice for over 10 years. She continues to practice as a psychotherapist in Fort Collins, Colorado. Please visit stacymusial.com for more information about her services.

Made in the USA
Coppell, TX
14 February 2023

12817156R00077